TOP SECRET BOEING

TOP SECRET BOEING

The life story of an elderly American airliner, a
Boeing 247-D, a gift from Canada to Britain, which
flew with the RAF to play a key part in winning the
Radar Battles of the Second World War

Bob Shaw

Defford Airfield Heritage Group

Published by the author on behalf of The Defford Airfield Heritage Group.

E-mail contact: r29shaw@o2.co.uk
Web-site: http://deffordairfieldheritagegroup.wordpress.com

British Library Cataloguing in Publication Data.
A catalogue record of this book is available from the British Library.

ISBN 978-0-9547045-1-3

Printed by Quorum Print Services Ltd.,
Units 3 & 4, Lansdown Industrial Estate,
Gloucester Road, Cheltenham , Glos. GL51 8PL

**Cover painting by Colin Doggett, showing the Boeing 247-D
DZ203 over Defford Airfield and Croome Park,
with the Malvern Hills in the distance.**

I sometimes wonder if the Americans are aware of the great contribution made to the war effort by this docile slow aircraft...

Group Captain Frank Griffiths DFC, AFC, Légion d'Honneur, Croix de Guerre

The most valuable cargo ever brought to our shores.

J P Baxter, 'Scientists Against Time', 1946

We were able to home the Boeing from 50 miles range, orbit the airfield at a selected range, line up with the runway and land, all on the auto-approach system – results not previously achieved in any sphere of aviation at that time (1945).

Group Captain John A McDonald CBE, AFC

Contents

Acknowledgements   9

Foreword   13

1. A Very Singular Aeroplane   17

2. Learning to See in the Dark   23

3. The Boeing 247 – The First Modern Airliner   29

4. Boeing 247 NC13344 in US Airline Service   33

5. In Canadian Service   55

6. The Boeing in Britain   73

7. A New Challenge – Exploring the X-Band   95

8. Automatic Blind Landing   121

9. PICAO Swansong   165

10. BLEU and the Demise of the Boeing   173

Appendix A – How Many Hours did the Boeing Fly?   187

Appendix B – What did the Boeing in Britain Look Like?   191

Appendix C – What Remains?   195

Abbreviations   199

Index   203

References and End Notes   207

Acknowledgements

I am indebted to a great number of people, and many organisations, who have provided information, archive material and photographs.

I am particularly grateful though to two people who have given me exceptional support during the preparation of this book.

Firstly, Dr Dennis Williams, a fellow member of the Defford Airfield Heritage Group, who not only made available the output of his own research and gave access to his records, but also read through and offered corrections to succeeding drafts of this book, and helped me in every way to prepare it for publication.

Secondly, Terry Judge in Canada who generously provided the outcome of his own research, forwarding documents which he had to laboriously copy out at the national archive in Canada, and read through the draft, challenged some of my assumptions, and provided corrections and suggestions of further information to include.

In the United States, I am especially grateful to Michael J Lombardi of the Boeing Company, and to Marvin Berryman, United Airlines Historical Foundation. Thanks also to Walter Binkley of the Aircraft Registration Branch of the Federal Aviation Administration for supply of a facsimile of the records file of NC13344; Dan Hagedorn and Katherine Williams at The Museum of Flight, Seattle; Robert van der Linden and Elizabeth Borja at the National Air and Space Museum; Suzi Taylor, Wyoming State Archive; Tamsen Hert, University of Wyoming Libraries; Melissa Keisser, Smithsonian Institution; Theresa Smith of the MIT Museum; and Miriam Lewis at The Institute of Navigation, for permission to quote from the paper by Frank B Brady. In Canada, grateful thanks to Carl Vincent for photographs and information, and to Nancy Fay at Libraries and Archives Canada for permission to reproduce drawings.

In the United Kingdom, particular thanks are due to Ron Henry, Phil Butler and Sqn Ldr Mike Dean, who reviewed the book in draft, and supplied information, many photographs and a great deal of helpful advice, especially on radar science and technology, and the history of TRE at Malvern and TFU at Defford.

Thanks also to other members of the Defford Airfield Heritage Group, including Graham Evans, Stephen Reglar, Roger Wintle, Mike Freer and Antony Whitehead, and to Albert Shorrock and members of the RAF Defford Reunion Association, the National Trust at Croome, and the Friends of Croome Park.

Members of Air Britain provided useful information through the medium of the AB-IX network, notably Geoffrey Negus, Peter Berry, John M Davis, Dave Welch, Maurice Wickstead, Alan Smith and Robert Parmerter.

Especial thanks are due to Lloyd Cromwell Griffiths for access to the logbooks and papers of his father, Gp Capt Frank Griffiths, for permission to quote from his father's book 'Angel Visits', and for writing the Foreword for this book. Thanks to Michael McDonald, for access to the flying logbooks and papers of his father, Gp Capt J A McDonald; to Mrs Lindsay Corr for the portrait photograph and copy of the logbook of her father, Flt Lt K B Hollowell; to Roger Knowles for access to the logbooks, photographs and papers of his father, Flt Lt Eric Knowles; and particularly, to Robert Fisher for access to the photo archives of his father Douglas Fisher, and for his permission to use photographs from his father's collection.

Thanks are due to Robert Hale Ltd, publishers, for permission to quote and use a photo from 'The Radar Army' by Reg Batt; Sir Bernard Lovell for permission to quote from his book 'Echoes of War', and Sir Bernard's P.A., Janet Eaton; Edward Bowen for permission to quote from 'Radar Days' by his father, E G 'Taffy' Bowen.

I have tried without success to contact the families of the late Reg Batt and the late J R Atkinson.

A considerable number of photographs in this book would have been Crown copyright, whatever their more recent provenance. However, following the advice in the National Archives leaflet on copyright which states that for photographs created before 1st June 1957, Crown copyright has expired, the credits on these photographs are worded accordingly.

This book could not have been written without access to The National Archives at Kew, also other libraries and archives, including the Royal Air Force Museum; the Imperial War Museum; The National Aerospace Library, Farnborough; the FAST Museum Archive, Farnborough; and Worcestershire County Libraries.

Many other people and organisations helped in so many ways – Ian White, author of 'Air Intercept Radar' (Pen & Sword); Alan Smith of the Martlesham Tower Museum; Mike Grant of the Wartime Aircraft Recovery Group Museum at Sleap Airfield; Mark Evans of the Midland Aircraft Recovery Group; Neville Cullingford of the Royal Observer Corps Museum; Marta Leskard and Neil Gray at the Science Museum, Wroughton; Mrs Mary Wain at the Bawdsey Radar Museum; Dr. Bill Penley and colleagues at the Purbeck Radar Museum Trust; and Roy Easson, formerly of BLEU.

Last but not least, my family – wife Pam, daughter Jane, son Geoffrey – who in many different ways, gave valuable help in the preparation of this book.

It is difficult to thank adequately all who have helped, and I may very well have failed to mention everyone who deserves my thanks, in which case for any shortcomings on my part in this direction, please accept my sincere apologies.

Note: References to sources cited are provided at the end of the book under the heading of References and Endnotes. In general I have only cited a reference once, the first time that there occurs a need to identify my source of information, and avoided citing references in support of every statement thereafter.   So the list of References (which by my own choice, does not conform to the Harvard System for references), is more of a Bibliography, but will still I hope be useful to the reader, and give some indication of the sources of information I have used in this book.

Bob Shaw
February 2012

Foreword

By Capt. Lloyd Cromwell Griffiths

At 1000 foot Radio Altitude above a very foggy Heathrow Common, shortly after 0600 hours on a black November morning, I call out "Auto Land; I have Control", and take over from my Co-pilot. She has been following the instructions of the Heathrow Approach Controller (the best in the world) and our Boeing 767 is perfectly aligned on Glideslope and Azimuth for Runway 09 Left at London Heathrow. We have over 90 seconds to touch down but no further words will be spoken between us as the Co-pilot continues to monitor the Instruments. I maintain a watch on our height and speed but inevitably I am drawn to peering ahead into the thick fog as I anticipate my first glimpse of the Approach Lights which will confirm what the cockpit instrumentation is telling us. Despite the Control Tower turning the lights up to full brightness the automated "ONE HUNDRED" foot call passes with no visual contact. Now I am seeking my first blurred glimpse of a Runway Centre Line Light as it flashes under the nosewheel. Behind us a full load of passengers are slowly awakening after a short night flight from New York. Most have spurned breakfast in exchange for an extra thirty minutes sleep and they obediently sit with their seat backs upright, their tables stowed away and their seat belts fastened. Their thoughts are already turning to the next leg of the journey. Roads and railways are going to be disrupted by the thick fog which is blanketing Southern England.

Looking ahead from the Flight Deck, the Landing Lights reflect back off the fog. They are not helping, and turning them off is an option, but the disorientating discotheque reflection of the flashing white strobe lights will then become more apparent. We are in our own world with no visual clues and crossing the ground which is less than 100 feet below us at well over 140 miles an hour.

"FIFTY, THIRTY, TWENTY", the Thrust Levers gently retard as the nose of the Boeing gently pitches up into the Flare. A blur of runway lights flash by under the nose. The automatic voice calls out "TEN" and seconds later the main wheels rumble onto the tarmac straddling the Centre Line lights. The nose lowers, a little abruptly for my liking, and the rumbling nose wheels confirm that the Boeing 767 is exactly on the centre line of the runway as they gently thump along the Runway Centre Line lights. The Speedbrakes deploy above the top surface of the wing and kill the lift whilst the Autobrake gently bites as we pull Reverse Idle on the Engines and the Boeing slows to a walking pace. Only now am I happy to disconnect the Autopilot and take over the aircraft.

An Auto Land is a routine operation for an airline pilot but always extra satisfying for me as the proud possessor of my father's flying Log Books, which record on the 16th January 1945: "THE Demonstration Flight ticked. First Auto Landing". The aircraft that made that historic landing was also a Boeing, recorded as DZ203, a Boeing 247-D.

The same Log Books record that my father, Group Captain Frank Griffiths, flew 67 different aircraft types. Spitfire, Hurricane, Walrus, Halifax and the roll call of iconic Second World War aircraft goes on and on. The names roll off the tongue but none of them generated as much affection and loyalty as DZ203, the rather staid but very kindly mannered Boeing 247-D on which my father recorded so many flights over several years of the war.

I am delighted to have been asked to write the Foreword to this book because I know that it is a role that my late father would have relished. Bob Shaw, the author, has taken the tale of a "very singular aeroplane", DZ203, an ex-airlines Boeing 247-D, as his loom and on it has woven a compelling tapestry which tells the story of three of the most significant British scientific contributions to the Second World War. This unique aircraft was the flying test bench for the development of the American 10 cm radar based on the British magnetron for detection of enemy aircraft, the demonstration of 3 cm radar (X-Band) for the detection of U-boat snorkels, and finally the proving of the world's first Auto Land system.

This book is more than the story of a very special aircraft. It brings to life the personalities who, driven by the urgency of war and led by the remarkably far-sighted Group Captain McDonald, took their ingenious ideas from the research bench on to Operational Test Flying and into production on the Allied air armada. It is a long overdue tribute to the genius and ingenuity of the Boffins and the tenacity and skill of the test pilots. Impatient with red tape and politics, this was a team that delivered vital operating systems for aircraft and pilots which significantly swung the air war in favour of the Allies.

My father's flying tales were always well told and invariably full of humour. He imbued me with a love of aviation which has stayed with me for over forty years of flying float planes, ski planes, crop sprayers and passenger turbo prop and jet aircraft. My early years in aviation were spent in the Canadian Arctic flying ski and float planes. These were "bush" aircraft landing on skis or floats on the remote lakes and rivers of the High Arctic. The Bush Pilot's fear was to be caught "on top" above cloud or fog with diminishing fuel reserves and no means of making a successful visual descent to sea level. Twenty five years on from my father's first Auto Land in 1945, I was posted to Hudson's Bay to replace a pilot who had crashed and been killed when forced to descend blind through impenetrable fog onto sea ice. The dangers inherent to flying have remained the same since the Wright brothers first flew.

Later in my career when I was fortunate to be given the responsibility for the Flying Operations of our national carrier, I commanded a number of Royal and Prime Ministerial Flights to our far flung Commonwealth. One particularly joyful Royal Tour was to South Africa following Nelson Mandela's release. The joy of the Rainbow Nation was infectious and occasionally hilarious. The demanding schedule allowed no leeway and on more than one occasion I muttered a silent thank you to the development of radar as we weaved our way between the towering thunderheads of the Inter Tropical Convergence Zone – the home of the thunderstorm! Invisible to the naked eye on a dark night over central Africa but faithfully "painting" an eye catching and threatening red "return" on our radar screens. I have never experienced the satisfaction of spotting the radar return from a submarine snorkel, but the wartime Boffins and airmen who flew on that much earlier Boeing, DZ203, would take enormous satisfaction from the long lasting peacetime applications of their vital war work.

Drive past any busy major airport in the world and you will see a staircase of modern passenger jets stretching back up into the sky as far as the eye can see. On a single runway those jets will be landing at intervals of less than a minute and a half. If the fog rolls in then they will still be landing, but now there will be at least three minutes between landing aircraft. Radar and Auto Land have made all that not only possible but so safe and routine that the passengers are more concerned about retrieving their bags on arrival than they are about the ability of the aircraft to return them safely to the ground in zero visibility.

Bob Shaw's book engagingly tells the story of the ingenuity of the scientists and the skills of the pilots in the development of Radar and Auto Land. The scientists flew on the aircraft testing their own inventions and displaying the same courage and impatience to make progress that drove on the pilots. My father was a very modest man. He flew many hours at the controls of Boeing DZ203 testing and developing the radar that would play such a key role in protecting Britain from the German night bomber and U Boat threats. Over those long hours he developed a harmony with the old Boeing that gave him the confidence (after a false start which he typically described as a fiasco!) and the courage to take his hands and feet off the controls and to watch this "singular aeroplane" gracefully descend in a smooth and stable trajectory to land herself on the runway at Defford. No wonder he felt that this aircraft, above all the many types that he flew, had a real soul.

This book does justice to the soul of that old Boeing and to the achievements of the men and women of RAF Defford.

1. A VERY SINGULAR AEROPLANE

RAF Defford in Worcestershire was one of the most important and most secret places in Britain during the Second World War.

Defford airfield opened for flying in September 1941. Initially it was a satellite airfield for No. 23 Operational Training Unit (OTU) at Pershore. But in May 1942, Defford became the new home for the Telecommunications Flying Unit (TFU), which operated aircraft on behalf of the Telecommunications Research Establishment (TRE) whose radar laboratories and workshops had moved at short notice from Worth Matravers near Swanage in Dorset, to Malvern in Worcestershire. RAF Defford was conveniently situated, a dozen miles or so from Malvern. The TFU had previously been based first at Christchurch and then at Hurn in order to serve TRE when it was at Worth Matravers.

From May 1942 onwards, an enormous number and variety of aircraft came and went at Defford, where they took part in radar experiments, mainly using apparatus manufactured in the workshops at TRE, while other aircraft were fitted with radar systems produced in small quantities for operational use.

Almost all these aircraft were military types, mainly from the RAF, but also from the Fleet Air Arm and US Army Air Forces, modified to take radar installations. An exception to this plethora of military types was an elderly American airliner, a Boeing 247-D which was given the British serial number DZ203 when it arrived in Britain in 1941, and which then moved to Defford with the TFU from Hurn in May 1942. This Boeing was intensively used at TFU throughout the war, only to meet its end in circumstances on which accounts vary, in the harsh winter of 1946-47.

It may seem odd that an obsolete American airliner, the only one of its type in Europe, should have been shipped across the Atlantic at the height of the U-boat threat when shipping space was at a premium, and used so intensively throughout the war for radar research, when so many operational aircraft types were available in Britain.

A set of 'walk around' photos (of which four survive) of Boeing 247-D DZ203 was taken at Christchurch in August 1941, very soon after it arrived from the United States. Evidence of the American AI radar which was installed, can be seen in the bulge under the nose which accommodated the drive for the helical scanner. The original of each photograph in this set is marked on the lower right hand corner 'BOEING 247D WASP ENGINES AUG/41' (Crown copyright)

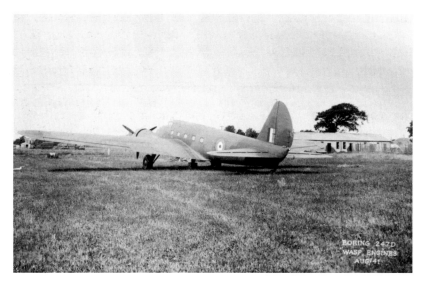

But there was a good reason why the 247-D was sent from America to Britain in July 1941; this was specifically because of the radar with which it had been fitted at the behest of the Tizard Mission to the United States. Thereafter it was held in high regard by pilots at the TFU, and by TRE scientists who preferred DZ203 for their research flying over all other available aircraft. Indeed, with some it went beyond high regard to positive affection. Dr Reg Batt, a scientist at TRE, in his memoirs[1] comments on the wide variety of aircraft at Defford, but says: *'... for those of our own group, nothing compared to our Boeing. Luxury indeed. Not for us the necessity to shin up through a tiny hatch in the belly of a fighting plane to crouch in close quarters to the equipment. We enjoyed armchair flying with our equipment spread liberally along a bench'.*

In an outstanding culmination of its service to wartime radar research, from late 1944 onwards, 'The Boeing' (as it was generally referred to at Defford) was found to be admirably suited to automatic landing trials. Later, after the demise of the Boeing, Group Captain Frank Griffiths wrote: *'The Boeing 247 was beloved of pilots... we were just lucky to have the placid Boeing. DZ203 proved to me that aeroplanes have souls. We had flown together for nearly five years ... I sometimes wonder if the Americans are aware of the great contribution made to the war effort by this docile slow aircraft, for it flew the first 10 cm radar which gave our night fighters a breakthrough, helped enormously in the research into submarine detection, and finally gave us the muscle to produce our own auto-landing system'.*[2]

The story of how Boeing 247-D, constructor's number (c/n) 1726, came to Britain begins in June 1940. France had fallen and Britain was in desperate straits. Winston Churchill had become Prime Minister, and he approved proposals from Sir Henry Tizard, the Chairman of the Aeronautical Research Committee, to seek the industrial help of the United States by sharing scientific secrets with the Americans, especially in the field of air defence. Churchill spoke to President Roosevelt directly about the need for a mission, and final negotiations for the visit were made by Lord Lothian, the British Ambassador in Washington. The proposition was agreed to by both

Continuing the set of 'walk around' photos of DZ203 taken in August 1941 at Christchurch, where the Boeing was now based in the care of the Special Duty Flight, which became the Telecommunications Flying Unit. On the western boundary of Christchurch aerodrome was the 'shadow' factory of Airspeed Ltd, whose buildings can be seen in the background.[3] (The Museum of Flight)

Governments, and the members of the mission under Tizard were selected in early August. Dr E G ('Taffy') Bowen, already a veteran of the pioneering airborne radar research work under Watson-Watt at Bawdsey Manor, was the radar specialist in the team, which sailed on 29th August, arriving at Halifax, Nova Scotia on 6th September 1940.

The purpose of the Mission was to hand over to the US Services details of the recent British technical advances including the jet engine and radar in its many forms.[4] It has to be remembered that at this time, the United States of America, was a neutral country.

Bowen carried with him one of the first examples of the resonant cavity magnetron, only recently invented by Howard Boot and John Randall at the University of Birmingham, which made possible the major advance of centimetre-wavelength radar. Tizard had insisted that Canada should be an equal partner in discussions with the United States and share in the technological secrets, and Bowen duly established contact with the Canadian National Research Council (NRC) in Ottawa, prior to meetings of the three countries in Washington. It was decided that work on centimetre-wavelength radar would be vested in the Microwave Committee of the US National Defence Research Council (NDRC), which organised manufacture of the magnetron based on the British design, at the Laboratory of the Bell Telephone Company. By November 1940, Bell had made 30 magnetrons, copied from the twelfth prototype of the eight-cavity magnetron type E1189, produced by the GEC Research Laboratory in Wembley, England, to the design of Boot and Randall.

The Radiation Laboratory at Massachusetts Institute of Technology (MIT) was established by NDRC to see through the centimetre-wavelength radar project, with a hangar and flight testing facility being provided at Boston Municipal Airport (later re-named Logan Field). By early 1941, the priority was to re-engineer the 10 cm wavelength units thus developed for use in airborne interception (AI), in a form suitable for aircraft installation, which was initially in a Douglas B-18, for trials. This was demonstrated very successfully, but there was an urgent need to get a working prototype of the US 10 cm radar to Britain for further demonstrations and trials. It was decided that this could best be done by fitting the radar in an aircraft, proving it and then sending the aircraft complete with the radar installed to Britain. The intention was to carry out the installation in a Douglas Boston aircraft, of the type already being supplied to Britain and adapted for use as the Havoc night fighter, but it was concluded that at this stage of development a larger aircraft was needed to accommodate the still bulky radar. In any event, Bowen stated that there was no Boston available from the British order at the right time. Meanwhile, the Canadian wing of the radar research triumvirate was already working on fitting the experimental 'AI-10' radar in a Boeing 247-D in order to carry out its own trials. In the words of E G Bowen *'... at this point the ever-willing Canadians came to the rescue and offered the Boeing 247-D'*, to be sent to Britain as a flying demonstrator of the 10 cm radar built in the United States as an outcome of British, American and Canadian co-operation.

Thus this Boeing 247-D (which had previously been NC13344 and then 7655 in Canada), came to Britain, to earn its place in aviation history as DZ203 with the RAF.

To explain more about the importance of RAF Defford, and the research work so vital to the war effort that was carried out there, it is necessary to go back a few years, to the origins of airborne radar in Britain.

2. LEARNING TO SEE IN THE DARK

The story of how radar (as it came to be called)[5] was developed in Britain has been told many times. The story of how, in a very close contest, the advent of radar enabled Britain to fend off Hitler's bombers in 1940, and how by constant and relentless innovation, keeping just ahead of the enemy, the application of the principles of radar in many forms, enabled the Allies to win the Second World War.

In December 1934, the scientist and former civil servant Sir Henry Tizard, who was by then Rector of Imperial College, was requested to set up a committee to find ways for the British defences to detect approaching aircraft. His committee consulted Robert Watson-Watt, the Director of the government's Radio Research Station at Slough. Arnold Wilkins, who was responsible to Watson-Watt, offered evidence suggesting that radio waves could be used to detect aircraft. Watson-Watt organised a demonstration on 26th February 1935, using the BBC VHF radio transmitter at Daventry and, with a Handley Page Heyford (K6902) as a target, showed that an aircraft could reflect radio waves, returning them as an echo to a receiver on the ground. Other countries, including the United States, had made similar observations, but none felt a need for aircraft detection as urgently as Britain, which faced a threat posed by the growing bomber strength of Nazi Germany. Air Vice-Marshal Sir Hugh Dowding, the Air Member for Research and Development at the Air Ministry, was quick to recognise the potential of 'radio location' and ensured funding for the setting up of what became the Air Ministry Research Establishment (AMRE) at the former artillery range at Orford Ness in Suffolk.[6] One of the first scientists to be recruited to work for Watson-Watt at Orford Ness, on what later came to be called radar, was a young graduate from the University College of Swansea, E G Bowen, who joined a team of just four people.

By the autumn of 1935 the team at Orford Ness, under the informal leadership of Arnold Wilkins, was able to demonstrate to Watson-Watt and the Tizard committee, the ability to track an aircraft (Westland Wallace K3673) to a distance of 60 miles.[7] By December

1935, the Treasury had earmarked £1 million for the establishment of five stations to provide air warning on the approaches to the Thames estuary. The first of these was to be in Suffolk on elevated ground near the mouth of the River Deben, in the grounds of Bawdsey Manor, which as the Bawdsey Research Station (BRS) became the home of the radar research team, together with scientists of the War Office's Air Defence Experimental Establishment (ADEE). By the outbreak of war in September 1939, a co-ordinated chain of radar stations and reporting systems had been established along the whole of the East Coast and most of the South Coast of England. Tizard and Dowding were confident that this would enable the RAF to repel daylight attacks.

However, there was as yet no defence against the night bomber, where the interceptor had to get close to the target to identify and attack it. Tizard foresaw this problem as early as 1936 and as an outcome Bowen was charged with making a start on developing airborne radar equipment that could be fitted to a night fighter, leaving Wilkins and the team to continue the development of ground-based detection systems. Still working at Bawdsey, Bowen set up trials with the Aeroplane and Armament Experimental Establishment (A&AEE) at the nearby aerodrome of RAF Martlesham Heath, where 'D' flight of the A&AEE Performance Section was established, dedicated to the radar experiments.

The first 'airborne radar' system actually comprised a transmitter located at Bawdsey, and a radar receiver installed in a Handley Page Heyford bomber (possibly K5184). The concept was that the Heyford's receiver would detect signals, reflected by a target aircraft, from the ground-based transmitter. By 1937, two Avro Ansons (K6260 and K8758) had been allocated to the project. In August of that year a true airborne radar system – comprising a transmitter and a receiver - had been installed in one of the Ansons and successfully demonstrated. Notably, it performed exceptionally well in detecting the British Fleet and its carrier-based aircraft on exercises in the North Sea, in foggy conditions which had grounded land-based Coastal Command aircraft.

Dr E.G. 'Taffy' Bowen was a pioneer of radar, working under Watson-Watt from 1935. He was leader of the team which designed the first airborne radars, based at Bawdsey Manor and flying from Martlesham Heath, 1937 – 1939. In 1940, he went to the United States and Canada as a member of the Tizard Mission that revealed to the Americans the secret of the magnetron, which made possible dramatic advances in radar. Bowen was directly responsible for the Boeing 247-D DZ203 coming to Britain. (Douglas Fisher collection)

From this work emerged two applications of airborne radar – Air to Surface Vessel (ASV) and Airborne Interception (AI). Towards the end of 1938, the Anson was proving too slow to simulate a night fighter, and AI research switched to using a pair of Fairey Battles (K9207 and K9208), while a Handley Page Harrow (K7021) was provided as a more realistic target aircraft. Work continued apace, with 'D' Flight at Martlesham Heath growing in size to serve the needs of the scientists at Bawdsey Manor. In mid-July 1939, two Bristol Blenheims (K7033 and K7034) arrived at 'D' Flight with urgent instructions that they should be fitted with AI radar for trials. At the time, a fighter version of the Blenheim had been improvised to serve as a night fighter, a role which it continued to fulfil until the arrival in service of the Beaufighter in late 1940. Soon more Blenheims, this time Mark IV aircraft, arrived at 'D' Flight to be fitted with AI radar for operational trials by 25 Squadron, starting in September 1939.

Following the outbreak of war, it was decided to transfer the establishment at Bawdsey Manor and its associated flying section away from the vulnerable east coast of England, so the establishment moved to Dundee in Scotland, with 'D' Flight which became the Special Duties Flight (SDF) going to Perth (Scone) aerodrome. This rather unsatisfactory arrangement lasted less than two months, and was succeeded by an even less satisfactory one when the SDF moved to RAF St Athan in South Wales. Eventually, in May 1940, the scientists were sent to Worth Matravers, near Swanage in Dorset where AMRE was re-named the Telecommunications Research Establishment (TRE), while the SDF settled in at Christchurch aerodrome, 24 miles away.

The former civil aerodrome at Christchurch turned out to be an unsuitable choice, the airfield being too small and lacking sufficient suitable buildings. So the SDF, and its expanding fleet of aircraft and personnel, moved yet again, to Hurn near Bournemouth, now only 12 miles from Worth Matravers, where the SDF changed its name to become the Telecommunications Flying Unit (TFU). The move to Hurn started in August 1941, but was not complete until November.

Meanwhile, some flying of the radar trials aircraft continued at Christchurch.

It seemingly did not occur to anyone in authority that carrying out radar research on the south coast of Dorset was even more vulnerable to enemy interference than it had been at Bawdsey. That is, until British airborne troops, accompanied by an heroic RAF radar technician, Flight Sergeant C W H Cox, were dropped by parachute onto a German ground radar station on the coast of France at Bruneval, on 27th February 1942. The raid was successful in its objective, capturing key parts of a German Wurzburg radar. The paratroops, C Company of 2 Para, commanded by Major J D Frost, withdrew by sea, together with Flt Sgt Cox and parts taken from the captured radar, to be examined by the TRE scientist D H Priest, who was a member of the seaborne party. This was rightly regarded as a great coup, but it suggested that if the British could do such a thing, so could the Germans, making the radar research establishment near Swanage extremely vulnerable. Also, it was realised that the South Coast location made gathering of electronic intelligence easy for the enemy. Accordingly, plans were made at short notice to move the whole establishment to Malvern in Worcestershire, where TRE would occupy the premises of Malvern College for the remainder of the war, the staff and pupils having been evacuated to Harrow School.

Having moved TRE to Malvern, it was vital that TFU move to a suitable aerodrome as near to Malvern as possible, and for this purpose RAF Defford was selected.

This turned out to be a wise choice. Defford was almost the ideal place to carry out secret airborne radar research. There were already three hard runways forming a typical triangular pattern, which had been laid in 1941, on requisitioned land that had previously been Defford Common. The RAF also requisitioned a large part of the adjacent Croome Park, taking most of its land to the east and south of Croome Court, the ancestral home of the Earls of Coventry. The Park had been created for the 6th Earl in the 1760s, by the legendary 'Capability' Brown, and formed a gently rolling landscape studded with oak trees. These trees provided good natural camouflage from airborne observation, and the huts accommodating the workshops, laboratories, stores and offices, and other buildings used by TFU spread rapidly under the trees and across the parkland, together with some of the hard-standings for aircraft.

Having established the background to the story in Britain of the Boeing 247-D DZ203, we now need to go back and trace the history of this aircraft from its American origins.

A scene at Defford in 1942. Flt Lt R H Mountford, one of the Boeing's pilots, returned from an experimental flight, reports to a Canadian Observer colleague who is armed with a clip-board. In the background, is the old boundary wall of Croome Park, where recently erected TRE and TFU buildings spread across the parkland under the cover of the trees. (Douglas Fisher Collection)

3. THE BOEING 247 – THE FIRST MODERN AIRLINER

When the first Boeing 247 made its maiden flight on 8th February 1933, it marked the beginning of a new era in passenger air travel, at speeds more than 50 mph faster than standard types then in service. The design provided, for the first time in commercial operations, a low-wing cantilever monoplane of all-metal construction with retractable undercarriage. Even more revolutionary, the 247 was ordered off the drawing board with no prototype, United Air Lines having ordered 60 to be built in accordance with Approved Type Certificate (ATC) 500, while the project was still at the mock-up stage. In the event, United and its constituent companies received 59 of these aircraft, the last ten being built as the improved 247-D model.

United Air Lines and the Boeing Airplane Company were both members of the same group, the United Aircraft and Transport Corporation. At the time the 247 order was placed (and until 1st May 1934), United Air Lines was not an operator as such, but a holding company for four airlines – Boeing Air Transport (BAT), Pacific Air Transport (PAT), National Air Transport (NAT) and Varney Air Lines – and aircraft in the initial batch of 247s were delivered variously to these four airlines. Following the break-up of the United group in May 1934, as a consequence of anti-trust laws, the first three of these companies (Varney having already been taken over by BAT) formed a reconstituted United Air Lines (UAL), which then became the only airline operating the Boeing 247.[8, 9] On 12th June 1933, a Boeing 247 of NAT, NC13308, left Newark on the aircraft's first transcontinental passenger flight.

Initially, the performance of the 247 was disappointing, but a marked improvement was achieved by replacing the original three-bladed fixed-pitch propellers with two-bladed variable pitch (two-position) propellers. After the first batch of 247s had been built, including one 247A executive version, and two ordered by Deutsches Lufthansa (DLH)[10], a further 15 aircraft were finished to the much improved 247-D standard.

The First Modern Airliner – NC13301, c/n 1682, the first Boeing 247, made its maiden flight at noon on 8th February 1933. (Marvin Berryman, United Airlines Historical Foundation)

The 247-D featured Pratt & Whitney Wasp S1H1-G geared and supercharged engines, driving three-bladed Hamilton Standard variable pitch (two-position) propellers, in place of the Wasp S1D1 engines of the original 247s. The nacelles were redesigned with full length NACA cowlings for the engines, with all engine accessories enclosed within the cowlings. This change of power installation resulted in a marked increase in performance. In addition, the aileron trim tabs were increased in span, and the vertical tail was redesigned with a straight rudder hinge line and separate balance tabs fitted to the rudder. The rudder and ailerons were covered with fabric rather than metal.[11,12] A number of other changes included improvements to heating and ventilation in the passenger cabin. Apart from the engines, the most obvious external change on the new-build 247-D was the replacement of the forward-sloping windscreen of the 247 with the more conventional rearward-sloping one. Subsequently, many, if not all, 247s were modified to 247-D standard, although it appears that of those modified, most retained the original forward-sloping windscreen design.

Three UAL Boeings in flight – NC13342, NC13359 and NC13334, after conversion to 247-D status in 1935. (Marvin Berryman, United Airlines Historical Foundation)

The 247-D earned worldwide fame in 1934, when Roscoe Turner flew a 247-D modified with extra fuel tanks, to second place in the Commercial section of the England-Australia 'MacRobertson' Air Race, coming third overall behind the de Havilland DH88 Comet and a KLM Douglas DC-2.

The Boeing 247-D enjoyed only a few years in the limelight, in service with the main airlines. It was rapidly overtaken and overshadowed by the larger and faster Douglas aircraft – first the DC-2, then the DC-3. By 1935, the 247 and the 247-D were being relegated to secondary airlines. Consequently, there were no further orders for the 247 after the 75 which had been completed by the end of 1934.

The configuration of the fin and rudder of a UAL Boeing 247 NC13309 (c/n 1690), before it was converted to 247-D standard in August 1935. Thereafter, it was leased out by UAL to various smaller airlines, before being impressed as a C-73 in 1942. (Marvin Berryman, United Airlines Historical Foundation)

This UAL Boeing 247-D seen at Salt Lake City, NC13334 (c/n 1716), was converted to 247-D standard in April 1935, shortly before sister ship NC13344 was transferred to Pennsylvania Airlines without being converted. (Marvin Berryman, United Airlines Historical Foundation)

4. BOEING 247 NC13344 IN U.S. AIRLINE SERVICE

One of the Boeing 247 aircraft from the first batch, which much later was modified from 247 to 247-D standard (but without changing the windscreen arrangement), bore the constructor's number c/n 1726, and was registered as NC13344. This aircraft was to become DZ203 with the RAF in 1941, and is the subject of this book.

The date of the first flight of NC13344 is not recorded[13], but the Bill of Sale for this aircraft to National Air Transport (NAT), is dated 17th July 1933, although it had been registered to NAT as early as 10th April 1933.[14] As already related, NAT was one of four airlines controlled by the United Aircraft and Transport Corporation, which received the Boeing 247 aircraft ordered by the United group. However, in 1934 all four companies were merged into one brand as United Air Lines (UAL).

An application by NAT for inspection of NC13344 for a commercial licence, dated 17th July 1933, states that the aircraft could be inspected at Boeing Field, Seattle. On 19th July 1933, the completed Operation Inspection Report (OIR) of the Bureau of Air Commerce confirms the owner as NAT. Under the heading of 'Total Aircraft flight time' is entered 'new airplane', indicating that NC13344 had not yet flown. The licence was issued under Approved Type Certificate (ATC) No. 500, recording an actual empty weight of 8,420 lb and the engines as 550 hp S1D1 Wasps, serial numbers R (right) 5250 and L (left) 5449, with propellers R21516 and L21515.

NC13344 was very soon fitted with variable-pitch propellers, in line with other 247s, resulting in a change of weight (now recorded in the 'License Authorisation' as 8,320 lb empty), and an OIR dated 4th August 1933, which recorded the new propellers with no change of engines. Flying time to date on 4th August is recorded as 97 hours in just over two weeks, which suggests NC13344 was already busily employed on the routes. By 20th October 1933, an OIR recorded total aircraft flight time as 609 hours over three months. This level of use (around 40-45 hours each week), continued into 1934, with the OIR reports, at roughly three month intervals, recording that the engines had been changed by the time each of these reports was filed. On 20th

July 1934, NC13344 was formally re-assigned to United Air Lines (UAL), following the restructuring of the United group business as previously outlined. UAL used its fleet of Boeing 247s on the coast to coast routes, typically Newark - Chicago - San Francisco, and throughout the UAL network. During the coast-to-coast flights, taking a total of 19 hours 30 minutes, passengers sat in the ten upholstered seats in a heated, noise-insulated cabin while cruising at 160 mph. There was a lavatory at the rear of the cabin and a hot meal buffet area situated on the port side, opposite the boarding door which was on the starboard side, aft of the wing. The crew consisted of pilot, co-pilot and stewardess, and NC13344 is recorded on OIRs at this time as a Model 247-13PCLM, indicating that it could carry 10 passengers plus 3 crew.

On 25th September 1934, NC13344 was returned by UAL to the Boeing Aircraft Company for fuselage repairs as part of a corrosion prevention programme. This involved replacing various members (channels, angles and catwalks), and the fitting of additional stiffeners. The new parts were in anodised Duralumin.

During the course of 1935, UAL undertook conversion to 247-D standard of at least 32 of the original 247 fleet, but NC13344 was not included in this programme of work. The unmodified 247s were sold or leased to smaller airlines whose routes fed directly into the UAL network. This trend continued as UAL was obliged to order larger, faster DC-2 and DC-3 aircraft which progressively replaced their 247 and 247-D aircraft in mainline service. NC13344 was in fact one of the first of the unconverted 247s to be transferred out by UAL, going to Pennsylvania Airlines, on 14th May 1935. NC13344 is still recorded at this date as a Model 247-13PCLM, showing that the flight attendant's position was retained in its specification.

On 5th June 1935, the Bureau of Air Commerce issued a Boeing 247 Loading Schedule for NC13344, marked: 'For use on Pennsylvania Airlines ONLY', adding cryptically 'No stewardess or de-icer included. Empty weight 8,720 lb, gross 13,100 lb'.

"Commuter's Service Between Chicago and New York."
United Air Lines Boeing 247 NC13344 on the ground at Chicago, Illinois, loading passengers, with engines running; circa September 1933. This photo was accompanied by a press release promoting 'Service every hour on the hour from 8:30 A.M. to 6:30 P.M. between America's two largest cities on a five-hour schedule - sixteen planes in each direction daily'. NC13344 was in service successively, with UAL, Pennsylvania Airlines, Pennsylvania-Central Airlines, Wyoming Air Service and Inland Air Lines until 1940, when it was sold to the Canadian government as CF-BTA, becoming serial number 7655 with the RCAF. It went to Britain in July 1941 as DZ203, a flying demonstrator for American AI-10 radar. (National Air and Space Museum, Smithsonian Institution, SI 2009-31647)

In February 1936, NC13344 gained national fame, of a sort, in magazines on news-stands across the country, where it appeared as the back drop for a Plymouth car advert. The name of Pennsylvania Airlines can be seen on the side of the fuselage in a logo which appeared rather similar to the generic logo used by UAL and by airlines in the United group.

An anonymous Boeing 247, after being fitted with twin-bladed VP propellers. NC13344 was thus converted in August 1933 after only 97 hours flying time since delivered to NAT in July 1933. (Marvin Berryman, United Airlines Historical Foundation)

An OIR dated 17th January 1936, made out to UAL, records NC13344 as a Model 247-12PCLM, confirming that for Pennsylvania Airlines, provision for a stewardess had been removed, her services not being required on the shorter routes now being flown. These routes however, included the stage from Detroit to Cleveland over Lake Erie, and the federal authorities required inflatable flotation gear to be installed. On 18th July 1936, an equipment list for NC13344 was compiled and filed with the Bureau of Air Commerce by W S Rosenberger, the Operations Manager of Pennsylvania Airlines. This included flotation gear and 12 life preservers. The document was

A rare photograph of NC13344 with Pennsylvania Airlines, providing the backdrop to a Plymouth car advert published in February 1936. NC13344 transferred from UAL to Pennsylvania Airlines in May 1935.

signed off by A Murphy, Department of Commerce Inspector, who issued a Bureau of Commerce Loading sheet for NC13344 showing the effect of the flotation gear, which weighed 340 lb, and raised the empty weight of the aircraft to 9,070 lb.

However, all was not well. A letter dated 7th August 1936 from the Manufacturing Inspection Service, to Pennsylvania Airlines & Transport Co, Cleveland, Ohio, stated bluntly that the airline's Boeing 247s equipped with flotation gear were not eligible for the issue of an annual licence because the equipment list was not satisfactory. The letter stated *'Airline Inspector Murphy has been given detailed instructions regarding correction of the list and will contact you'*. It was pointed out that not all inflatable flotation bags had been pressure tested – just four bags had been tested and only on NC13311, although both this aircraft and NC13344 (which had not been tested) had been granted a temporary licence. Annual licences could not be issued until these tests had been carried out on all six aircraft in the fleet, a total of 24 bags. It was insisted that Inspector Stephens should witness the testing personally, and not rely on the affidavit of the operator. Clearly, there was some mistrust of Pennsylvania Airlines on the part of the air regulation authorities.

On 20th August 1936, an Aircraft Inspection Report (AIR) was issued, made out to UAL as owners of the NC13344 although leased to Pennsylvania Airlines, following alterations in connection with the flotation gear. It was commented: *'Safety line installation checked in accordance with sketch. Installation and inspection was made in accordance with Navy specifications SR-4C'*.

Pennsylvania Airlines competed with Central Airlines on the busy routes to and from Detroit and Washington, and in November 1936, the two airlines merged to form Pennsylvania-Central Airlines (PCA), based on Allegheny County Airport, Pittsburgh, its fleet now emblazoned with the bold logo 'PCA'. This airline's heaviest traffic was on its main route which covered Norfolk-Washington-Pittsburgh-Cleveland-Detroit, with branches to Chicago, Milwaukee, Baltimore and Buffalo. The routes of PCA linked the major cities of the Middle Atlantic states with the Great Lakes, and as the line expanded during

NC13344 would have displayed a similar appearance to this Boeing 247-D when it served with PCA from November 1936. NC13358 was one of the aircraft obtained by PCA in 1937, to replace the six Boeings which went first to Robert Cuse, then to W L Monro Jnr, finally to be dispersed to various airlines in the United States and Mexico. (The Boeing Company)

the late 1930s, with the South. The acquisition of 247 and 247-D aircraft, initially on lease from UAL, played a major part in developing these routes.

The provision of flotation gear on the Boeings was clearly a contentious issue with Pennsylvania and now with PCA. There were various suggestions in the correspondence between the airline and the authorities, that the operator felt this provision was not necessary. The aircraft flew at 6,000 feet which it was argued, would in the event of engine failure allow the plane to glide to the shore from any point on the route over Lake Erie. Also the engines were very reliable, and risk of the failure of one engine let alone both over the lake was minimal. Robert van der Linden in his definitive history of the Boeing 247, says that pilots were not fond of the flotation device and quotes a former PCA pilot, Captain Edward P O'Donnell: *'We had a great mistrust of this type of installation ... we had a great fear of these* (inflatable) *bags being inadvertently deployed in the air, so we carried forty-fives* (0.45 inch calibre pistols) *with us just in case, so we could fill the sacks with holes'.*[15]

Had they been aware of this arrangement, passengers would no doubt have been reassured by the prospect of in-flight entertainment in the form of the captain and co-pilot blazing away with six-shooters within the confines of the aircraft.

However, it is not difficult to imagine a certain resentment of officialdom in this small airline, and a reluctance to add equipment which reduced potential payload, and was seen as unnecessary and possibly dangerous. But this may have had repercussions in relationships with the federal authorities.

On 8th December 1936, the Bureau of Air Commerce recorded 'major repairs' to NC13344. The drawings accompanying the Repair and Alteration Form show details of a splice in the tubular steel construction of the left motor mounting. There is no evidence as to what caused the need for this repair or where the remedial work was carried out, but the form is signed by W S Rosenberger, the Operations Manager of PCA at Cleveland Airport, and approved by the Department of Commerce Inspector following receipt on 28th December 1936.

Meanwhile, tragic events were unfolding in Europe as Spain sank into a bitter civil war. Both sides in the conflict were keen to buy aircraft, including civil types which could be adapted to an offensive role. Robert Cuse, the head of the Vimalert Company, a second-hand aircraft and arms dealer, realised that there was an opportunity to sell arms to the Republican side in the civil war. He also realised there was no law to prevent him doing so. The United States Neutrality Act of 1935 prohibited the export from the United States of arms where two countries were at war – but as Cuse and his legal advisers pointed out, this was not the case in Spain. On 28th December 1936, he obtained a licence from the State Department to sell $2,777,000 worth of aircraft, engines and parts to the Spanish Republicans.

The licence covered 18 aircraft – seven Vultee V1As, two Northrop Deltas, one Fairchild 91 and one Lockheed 10 Electra, plus the one and only Douglas DC-1, and no less than six Boeing 247 aircraft. For the purpose of the licence, the Boeings were priced at $35,000 each. Amongst these was NC13344, in fact the six aircraft listed represented the entire Boeing fleet of PCA. Also itemised on the licence were 411 aero engines, including 80 Wasp R-1340 engines.[16] It is reported that all the 18 aircraft were gathered together and crated at North Beach airport on Long Island, preparatory to shipping to Spain. The position of the United States government was that supplying either side in the Spanish conflict was contrary to the intent of the law. President Roosevelt and the State Department denounced Cuse and insisted that Congress take action. In the event only eight of the aircraft (four Vultees, the two Deltas, the Electra and the Fairchild 91), were loaded on the Spanish ship *Mar Cantábrico* which departed New York docks on 7th January 1937, just succeeding in reaching international waters to escape the embargo against arms for Spain voted by Congress, but leaving ten aircraft, including the six Boeings, on the quay.[17] In the event, the *Mar Cantábrico* was intercepted by Nationalist warships, and the cargo passed into Nationalist hands. There is no evidence, in the FAA file or elsewhere, that ownership of NC13344 and the other Boeings was actually transferred to Cuse or his company Vimalert.

Had the deal gone through and not been prevented by Congress, and had NC13344 gone to Spain, that particular aircraft would not have gone on to distinguished service with the RAF in the Second World War. The Vultee V1A single-engine airliners that went to Spain in an earlier consignment were adapted by the Republicans as attack bombers, with fixed forward firing machine guns and dorsal defensive gun positions[18], and the Boeings would probably have been modified similarly had they reached Spain. There was a design precedent in the sole Boeing 247-Y (c/n 1952) which was modified from a UAL airliner (NC13366), with 0.5 inch calibre guns fore and aft, plus added fuel tanks and under-wing bomb racks, ordered in 1936 by a Chinese warlord and delivered to China in 1937.[19]

After the Spanish deal fell through, NC13344 and its sister ships which had been dismantled for shipment, remained the property of UAL and may have been returned to PCA, but it is not clear whether any went back into service with that airline, who presumably had arranged to replace these six Boeings when it was thought UAL had sold them to Cuse.

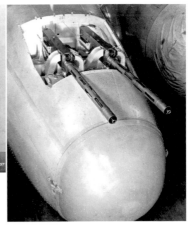

The armament fitted to the Boeing 247-Y, showing how NC13344 might have been modified had it gone to Spain. Left, above: The dorsal gun position. Right: *The nose compartment (which on DZ203 accommodated the radar scanner), housing fixed forward firing twin 0.5" guns with boxes for ammunition and spent cartridges below.* (The Boeing Company)

The interior of the 247-Y, with additional fuel tanks in the forward part of the cabin. This photo makes an interesting comparison with those in Chapter 8 showing the interior of DZ203 when it was equipped for auto-landing trials in 1945. (The Boeing Company)

However, the Airline Inspection branch of the Department of Commerce stepped in, on 21ˢᵗ January 1937 sending a cable to the Operations Manager of PCA at Cleveland Airport, worded as follows: *'Recent consolidation and transfers of your airline maintenance bases have resulted in maintenance inefficiencies which have led us to a finding of certain aircraft maintenance deemed unsafe for domestic scheduled airline operation in interstate air commerce. Therefore your letters of authority ... are hereby suspended effective immediately upon receipt of this notice to the extent of passenger carrying authority in your air line, (by aircraft) NC13303, 13308, 13311, 13331, 13344, 13356. You will at once cease all passenger carrying operations in such aircraft ... pending satisfactory inspection by the designated Inspector ... '.*

An Aircraft Inspection report on NC13344 dated 28ᵗʰ January 1937, concludes by recording that that the aircraft was *'not weighed on account of discontinuance in service'*. From this, it appears NC13344 had not resumed service with PCA. At this date, the aircraft had flown 6,663 hours.

The failure of the attempt to embark NC13344, and the other five Boeings from the PCA fleet, on the *Mar Cantábrico*, was not the last attempt to sell these aircraft to the Spanish Republicans. Soon, another opportunity occurred to send NC13344 to Spain.

On 3ʳᵈ March 1937, the ownership of NC13344 and its sister ships, was transferred from UAL to one W L Monro Jnr, who had the aircraft licences registered in his name as agent for John F Miller, George T Ladd, W L Monro, George A Blackmore, George R Hann and A W Robertson, with his address given as c/o The American Window Glass Co., Farmers' Bank Building, Pittsburgh, Pennsylvania. Then, in an undated copy of a cable addressed to the Department of Commerce Bureau of Aeronautics, which is on the FAA file, W L Monro Jnr and his associates, asserted their ownership of NC13303, NC13308, NC13311 and NC13331, presumably with the intention of selling them on. But for whatever reason, NC13344 and NC13356 were not listed in this cable.

At this point Robert Cuse comes back into the picture, purchasing three of the Boeings which Monro and his associates had very recently bought. Cuse was acting on behalf of Commandante José Melendreras Sierra, the Spanish Republican Purchasing Agent in the United States, who with his colleague Capitan Francisco Corral, arranged to purchase no less than 28 assorted aircraft in early 1937, with the intention of by-passing the embargo by flying them to Mexico. On 14th March, NC13356 flew to Vera Cruz in Mexico, followed by NC13331 and NC13303 on 17th March.[20] It has been reported that four Boeings flew to Mexico as part of the deal, but if this is true, the identity of the fourth 247 is not known. If it was one of the six former PCA Boeings, by a process of elimination it would have been NC13311, which by 1945 was with AVIANCA, the Columbian airline. The one other possible candidate was NC13308, but this it seems remained in the United States to be impressed as 42-57208, a C-73, in 1942.

NC13308 was one of the six Boeing 247s from the PCA fleet which, like NC13344, nearly went to the Civil War in Spain in the cargo ship Mar Cantábrico. *Here, NC13308 is seen in earlier and happier times, registered to Boeing Air Transport, probably taken during the summer of 1933, on show to a queue of visitors at a public open day. The nose hatch to the mail compartment is open for inspection. The aircraft has not yet been fitted with two-bladed variable pitch propellers, still having the initial three-bladed variety.* (Marvin Berryman, United Airlines Historical Foundation)

After what the author Gerald Howson[21] describes as '... *the most extraordinary tribulations through most of 1937* ...', the Ambassador in Mexico of the Spanish Republican Government, managed to ship out twelve of the 28 assorted aircraft on 29th December 1937. The ex-PCA Boeings though were not amongst this twelve, and remained in Mexico. With the other aircraft left behind, they were confiscated by the Mexican government, and sold to pay for the support of Spanish Republican refugees arriving in Mexico. The three Boeings became respectively XA-BFK, XA-BEZ and XA-BEY in Mexican airline service.[22]

It may have been that the intention of Monro and his associates when they bought the Boeings, was to sell all of them on to the Spanish Republicans, perhaps in association with Robert Cuse, but one can only speculate. However, after the flight of NC13303 and NC13331 on 17th March, the Federal authorities stepped in to stop any more such flights to Mexico, and as a consequence, NC13344 remained in the United States. Monro now had to seek other customers for the Boeings which he and his associates had acquired. Meanwhile, records suggest NC13344 did very little flying through the first eight months of 1937.

On 24th August 1937, the title of NC13344 was transferred by Monro and the individuals he represented, to Wyoming Air Service of Caspar, Wyoming, another airline with which United had concluded an arrangement. Wyoming Air Service operated a route from Billings in the north, through Cheyenne to Denver and on to Pueblo, but sold the Denver to Cheyenne section to UAL in late 1937. Wyoming operated a total of six 247s at various times, amongst these may have been NC13311, the second of the three ex-PCA Boeings which did not go to Mexico.

It will be noted, that unlike the case when the Boeing was with PCA, Wyoming Air Service was now the owner of NC13344. However, the UAL base at Cheyenne continued to maintain the Boeing, and in January 1938 major work was carried out on NC13344 at Cheyenne. In a completed Air Inspection Report form issued on 1st February, NC13344 had recorded 6,933 flying hours, having flown just 300

A poster for Wyoming Air Service, proclaiming the merits of the 3-mile-a-minute Boeing – note the assurance 'Veteran Pilots Always'! (Wyoming State Archives)

hours in the preceding 12 months, which included the hiatus following the Spanish episodes and the change of ownership. It was still an unconverted Model 247 but various modifications were now embodied which represented a start towards conversion to 247-D status. These are recorded in a Bureau of Air Commerce Repair and Alteration Form as having being carried out on 25th January 1938, received and signed off by the Aircraft Airworthiness office on 5th April. The work combined a major overhaul with alterations which represented part of the process of conversion from 247 to 247-D, including replacements and reinforcements to the wing stubs to 247-D standard, new wheel well linings, redecoration and sound proofing of the entire cabin, new heating and ventilation systems, and modifications to the fin and rudder in accordance with the approved

A Boeing 247-D of Wyoming Air Service, NC13350, a sister ship to NC13344. Both Boeings were with that airline and its successor Inland Air Lines, and both were sold to Canada in 1940. This photo was taken at Great Falls, MT, in 1938. NC13350, c/n 1951, was one of the first 247s to be converted to 247-D standard, in mid-1934, while NC13344 was one of the last. The work on NC13344 was carried out in stages over a period of over 12 months by UAL at Cheyenne and not completed to 247-D standard until August 1939, by which time Wyoming Air Service had become Inland Air Lines. (University of Wyoming, American Heritage Centre)

design for the 247-D. The landing gear was completely rebuilt, all electric wiring in the cockpit replaced, and sections of skin replaced on the fuselage aft of the cabin door. The flotation gear was removed. The Weight Check Sheet completed at UAL Cheyenne on 25th January 1938, noted non-standard equipment on NC13344, including 45 inch streamline Autofan wheels. The aircraft was fitted with re-capped tyres.

In July 1938, Wyoming Air Service changed its name to Inland Air Lines. On the 20th of that month the title of NC13344 was formally transferred to Inland Air Lines, who built up a small fleet of 247s, some of which continued to fly with Inland until 1943 when it merged with Western Airlines.

On 19th August 1938, further work was carried out at Cheyenne on the landing gear of NC13344. An overhauled engine was installed in the right nacelle, with an overhauled engine for the left nacelle following on 13th January 1939, by which time the aircraft had recorded 7,798 flying hours. Still NC13344 was recorded as a 247, not a 247-D.

Finally, a further round of repairs and alterations completed at Cheyenne on 5th August 1939, resulted in confirmation by affidavit that NC13344 conformed to 247-D standard under ATC number 558. The further work which had been required to complete the conversion included installation of nacelles to the new design, new cowlings, replacement of the fuel and oil lines, installation of electric inertia

Two Boeing 247-D aircraft of Wyoming Air Service in 1938, at the United Airlines Maintenance Depot at Cheyenne, where NC13344 in common with most former UAL Boeings, was serviced. The 247-D in the foreground has the back sloping windscreen of late models, but the 247-D in the background retains the windscreen with the forward rake, as on NC13344, and shows the appearance of NC13344 as it would have been after conversion to 247-D standard in stages between January 1938 and August 1939. (The Boeing Company)

starters, and modifications to the centre section of the wing. At the same time overhauled S1H1-G engines and propellers were fitted. NC13344 was now shown by internal placards to be a 247-D. In September 1939, the firewalls were replaced and the station 52 bulkhead reinforced.

NC13344 was overhauled and further modified at Cheyenne on 5th February 1940, when amongst other work, wing and empennage de-icer boots were installed, together with a new radio direction finder loop and receivers. On 15th May 1940, under Repairs and Alterations recorded, it was stated: *'Complete cockpit escape hatch skin replaced eliminating pyrolene window. This alteration was made by previous owner'.* There is no mention of this earlier modification anywhere in the records of NC13344, but the FAA file does tend to suggest that Pennsylvania Airlines and PCA may have been something of a law unto themselves when it came to unauthorised modifications. When the former NC13344 reached Britain in 1941, there was no window in the hatch over the cockpit, in common with most 247 and 247-D aircraft at that date.

A mystery which remains is that when this Boeing arrived in Britain as DZ203, it incorporated a square window in the main passenger door on the starboard side, which it retained for the rest of its life. It is not known by whom or when this installation was carried out. There is no mention of this alteration in the FAA file, so it may have been an unauthorised modification. This feature certainly was not present on NC13344 in 1933 as first built, and it is not known why the window was installed. There is photographic evidence that some other ex-PCA Boeings which subsequently went to the RCAF in 1940, had been so modified, including 7636, formerly NC13346, which was initially selected for the radar trials in Canada only for 7655 to be preferred for the task. Another of the ex-PCA Boeings which turned up in Canada was 7639, the former NC13350, which displayed a circular window in the door. Perhaps the added window was to give an outside view for the crew to check the situation on the ground after landing on the short stages flown by PCA – for instance, checking

In February 1940, NC13344, now with Inland Air Lines, was fitted with rubber de-icing boots to the leading edges of the wings and empennage at Cheyenne. This photograph shows work in progress, on a UAL 247-D similar in appearance to NC13344 at that time, fitting de-icing boots, in the UAL Maintenance Shop at Cheyenne (Marvin Berryman, United Airlines Historical Foundation)

that the passenger steps had been put in position before opening the door.

NC13344 made a final appearance in the workshops at Cheyenne on 9th August 1940, when the Autofan wheels were replaced by standard Warner wheels and brake assemblies, with new Goodrich Silvertown tyres, on standard Boeing 247-D axles. The record of all the work carried out at Cheyenne up to and including 9th August 1940, is useful in providing reliable documented information on the likely technical and mechanical condition of the airframe and equipment of the Boeing when it arrived in Britain in 1941.

The following day, 10th August 1940, the agent Charles H Babb completed arrangements whereby NC13344 was sold to the Canadian Government.

The Boeing was purchased by the Canadian Government together with seven more 247-Ds and various other twin-engine commercial aircraft, for use as trainers, in order to address a shortfall in supply of Anson aircraft for the British Commonwealth Air Training Plan (BCATP), which came into being in December 1939. Under the agreement setting up the Plan, Britain agreed to provide complete Anson aircraft, and subsequently to supply Ansons which would be fitted with wings made in Canada. However, the critical situation in Europe by May 1940, with the German invasion of Denmark, Norway, Belgium and the Netherlands being followed by the fall of France, resulted in a delay in supply of Ansons in any form from Britain. This was a potential disaster for the BCATP, since a number of twin-engine Service Flying Training Schools were about to open, and Britain was already behind in the delivery of the Ansons. As of 3rd June 1940 only 59 of the scheduled 90 Ansons had been delivered.[23]

The long term solution involved the production of complete Ansons in Canada, and the purchase of Cessna T-50 (Crane) aircraft from the United States. In the meantime the RCAF had the problem of where to find twin-engine trainers to make up the shortfall. To address this, it was decided to purchase 40 second-hand aircraft from the United States. The request was forwarded to the British Purchasing Commission (BPC) in New York, which was responsible for all war materiel bought in the United States, and they, in turn, asked the Charles H Babb Company to find suitable aircraft, starting in June 1940. In the end, 42 aircraft were purchased, among them eight Boeing 247s, including NC13344.

Charles H Babb then produced a series of 'profiles' of the aircraft he had located, listing the technical details of each aircraft, plus their asking price. These profiles were submitted to the BPC whose representative signed them off as 'accepted'. The profile for NC13344 was signed off by the BPC representative who inspected it at Cheyenne on 31st July 1940.[24]

A Bill of Sale dated 30th July, records that the Charles H Babb Company of 444 Madison Avenue, New York, sold NC13344 to the Department of National Defence of the Canadian Government in Ottawa, for $32,500, while another Bill of Sale shows that Charles H Babb purchased NC13344 from Inland Air Lines on 10th August 1940, for $27,500. In other words, Babb sold the Boeing to the Canadian Government twelve days before he bought it from Inland, and made $5,000 gross profit on the deal. Despite this, Inland were no doubt pleased and relieved to sell NC13344 for what seemed a good price, as two months previously on 31st May 1940, the entire Inland fleet of six Boeings was mortgaged for twelve months to the Stock Growers National Bank of Cheyenne and Casper National Bank of Casper, for the sum of $60,000 covering the six aircraft. Boeing 247-D NC13344 was subject to a partial release dated 7th August 1940 from the Stock Growers National Bank, in time for Inland to close the deal with Babb on 8th August.

The second-hand airliners purchased in 1940 from various American sources on behalf of the Canadian government by the agent, Charles H Babb, including the eight Boeing 247-D aircraft, now had to be brought into Canada. In passing, it should be noted that because Britain had agreed to provide or pay for aircraft to be used in the BCATP, the Boeings and other civil aircraft purchased in lieu of Ansons, through the BPC, were actually now British property, albeit for use by and in Canada.[25]

In Canada there had been a prohibition, since 1933, on the importation of second-hand aircraft. Fortunately, these customs regulations did not extend to second-hand aircraft acquired by the Canadian Government, so there appeared to be no impediment to their transfer to Canada. Presumably the entire situation had been carefully examined by both sides early in the process and found acceptable. As a result, starting in June 1940, the Department of Transport allotted certain ranges of registration marks to the Department of Munitions and Supply to be applied for the delivery of these aircraft, on the understanding that, after this use, the marks would be cancelled.[26]

NC13344 was assigned registration CF-BTA as early as July 1940, from the block CF-BSS to CF-BTQ allotted. However, unlike in the

UK, the allotment of a registration did not mean that this aircraft was 'registered' on the Canadian Civil Aircraft Register. In order to be 'registered' in Canada, an aircraft also had to be issued with a Certificate of Registration. Trans Canada Airlines had been awarded the contract to ferry all these aircraft from the United States into Canada, and although there is no record of the arrival of Boeing 247-D CF-BTA in Canada, it is assumed that its destination was RCAF Station at Trenton in Ontario.

CF-BTA was allocated the RCAF serial number 7655, and on 11th September 1940 was taken on strength by No. 1 Training Command.[27] However, all the imported aircraft flew in their temporary civil marks for a varying amount of time before having their RCAF serials applied.

The licence of NC13344 in the United States was cancelled on 3rd September 1940, when the aircraft was recorded as 'sold outside the US'.

It was the intention of the RCAF to use the eight 247-D aircraft for observer (navigator) training and as twin-engine pilot conversion trainers, but when distributed to a number of units, their reception was mixed. By September 1940, Britain had recommenced the delivery of Ansons to Canada, although there continued to be a shortage of twin-engine trainers for quite some time. Nevertheless, with the increasing availability of Ansons as standard trainers, it appears little use was found for the Boeings in this capacity. Most of the Boeings moved on to communications flights in the maritime and prairie provinces before being sold or leased to commercial firms from 1941 onwards. Maritime Central Airways purchased one, and five went to Canadian Pacific Air Lines and that company's smaller airline associates. Of the remaining two, one was scrapped, and the other was RCAF 7655, formerly NC13344. Its initial use with the RCAF has not been recorded but it is presumed to have stayed at Trenton and been flown there by the Central Flying School. However, this obscurity was about to change.

A magnificent photograph from the Boeing Corporate Archives, showing the appearance of the interior of the cockpit of a Boeing 247-D – in this case, c/n 1952, formerly NC13366, the one-off 247-Y for China, seen on 16th February 1937. Military equipment items, including bomb release controls, have been added to the left of the pilot's seat below the side windows, but otherwise the instrument panel and the controls appear similar to or the same as, those fitted in commercial service, for instance in NC13344. (The Boeing Company)

5. IN CANADIAN SERVICE

The arrival of Dr E H Bowen and the resonant cavity magnetron had a very considerable impact in both the United States and Canada.

The visit of the Tizard Mission (more properly the British Technical and Scientific Mission), to North America in the autumn of 1940 was a pivotal event in the war. The Mission unilaterally delivered to the Americans many of Britain's scientific secrets. This act of faith brought rich returns, in that the British learned much from the Americans in response. It also made the British more aware of scientific developments in Canada, and the part Canada could play in the war, especially in radar development. Winston Churchill and President Roosevelt agreed to jointly develop the scientific and technical means to prosecute the war against Germany, which resulted most importantly in harnessing of the scientific and industrial might of the United States to this end. In June 1940 Roosevelt had set up the National Defence Research Council (NDRC), with Vannevar Bush as Chairman. The NDRC was tasked with co-ordinating the research efforts of both military and civil scientists in the United States.

Sir Henry Tizard had been briefed by Professor A V Hill who had made an earlier visit to North America, in May 1940. Archibald Vivian Hill was a distinguished scientist, a Nobel Prize winner in 1922, who had been involved with Tizard since the earliest days of radar. Hill toured the United States in the hope that the American scientific research establishment might be encouraged to benefit the war effort. When he visited the National Research Council (NRC) in Ottawa he found a small but active group, under John T Henderson, working on radar. On his return to Britain from North America, Hill wrote a number of memos, one of which was entitled 'Research and Development for War Purposes in Canada'. In this memo, Hill urged that a high-level scientific liaison officer should be sent to Canada at once. This was acted upon and Professor Ralph H Fowler was appointed, arriving in Ottawa in early July 1940. Fowler, from the Department of Physics at the Cavendish Laboratory of Cambridge University, was working with the Ordnance Board in Britain at the time.[28]

Tizard and a colleague left England by flying boat (believed to have been the Short S.30 'Clare' G-AFCZ) on 14th August 1940[29] and, after arriving in Montreal, went on to Ottawa for meetings. Like Hill, Tizard was greatly impressed by the Canadians. In the meantime the remaining members of the Mission left England by sea on the 29th August, landing at Halifax on 6th September and, except for Bowen and his colleague Professor Cockcroft, travelled by train to Washington where they met up with Tizard. Meanwhile, Bowen and Cockcroft made a short visit to Ottawa which served to emphasise that the Canadians were now confirmed as equal partners in the outcome of the Mission.

The meetings between the Tizard Mission members and the Americans started on 10th September, and proved an eye-opener for both sides. One of the highlights was the demonstration of the resonant cavity magnetron by 'Taffy' Bowen. The Canadians were represented by C J Mackenzie, the Acting President of the NRC, who arrived in Washington on 11th September (the President of the NRC, Gen A G L McNaughton, had taken leave of absence in October 1939 to assume command of the 1st Canadian Division, which he took to Britain in December of that year). The next day, 11th September, Mackenzie telegraphed Ottawa asking that John Henderson immediately come to Washington.

As a result of these meetings, the NDRC set up the Microwave Committee under Alfred Lee Loomis who, in turn, used his considerable skills to organise the founding of the Radiation Laboratory at the Massachusetts Institute of Technology (MIT). The Radiation Laboratory (the vague name being a deliberate smoke-screen) was opened at the beginning of November 1940 and was headed by Dr Lee DuBridge. As an immediate priority, it was decided that the Radiation Laboratory would build five 10 cm wavelength radar sets, to an American design for an AI radar based on the British magnetron. One of these AI sets would go to Canada for trials. Vannevar Bush immediately contacted Mackenzie in Ottawa with an offer to the NRC for some of their staff to work at the Radiation Laboratory. This offer was taken up, and on 6th January 1941 six NRC staff members from the Radio Section of the Division of Physics and

Electrical Engineering arrived at the Radiation Laboratory to work on the 10 cm project. One of these men was F J Heath who was assigned to the transmitter group.[30]

The decision was also made that when the 10 cm radar sets became available for trials, these would take place concurrently in the United States and Canada. To test these first airborne units, an aircraft was needed that was large enough to accommodate the equipment, and the scientists and technicians to operate it. The prototype 10 cm AI radar apparatus was bulky and 'rather heavy' and needed an aircraft somewhat larger than any night fighter type then available. For this purpose the Americans chose a Douglas B-18, an obsolescent twin-engine bomber.

On 4th November, Fowler wrote to Mackenzie, briefing him on the progress that was being made in the 10 cm AI project, pointing out that a decision had to be made about obtaining a suitable Canadian aircraft in which to mount the new equipment. Fowler later met with Gp Capt Ferrier to discuss the situation, and on 19th November Fowler again briefed Mackenzie, reporting that Ferrier had suggested the use of a Boeing 247-D.[31]

The Boeing was preferred to any of the military types available in Canada, because of the considerable advantages it offered. It had a roomy cabin for the equipment and technicians, and side-by-side seating for the pilot and the observer or radar operator. The baggage compartment in the nose, with the hinged nose cone opening as an access hatch, offered convenient unobstructed space to accommodate the large, circular parabolic dish mounted on the scanner of the American 10 cm radar. In airline service, the nose compartment had provided a space of 60 cu ft capacity for luggage or parcels, while the rear upper part of this compartment housed the commercial radio equipment.

Ferrier's recommendation was acted upon immediately, as an exchange of notes between some of the Air Members of the (Canadian) Air Council shows.[32]

This contemporary cut-away drawing shows the interior of a Boeing 247 in UAL service. It shows some features of the aircraft which facilitated the conversion of RCAF 7655 to use for radar trials and research in Canada, and then as DZ203 in Britain. The nose compartment used for mail, was adapted to house radar equipment (in airline service the radio equipment was mounted in the top rear space of this compartment). Two pilots were seated side-by-side, which became particularly convenient when radar trials involved cockpit mounted indicators. The cabin for ten passengers with stewardess and her station to the rear, was converted to a flying workshop-cum-laboratory. Further aft can be seen the toilet with skylight over, and the rear luggage compartment, both these areas were used at various times to house Auxiliary Power Units to provide power for the radar equipment.

On 20th November 1940, the following request was received from the Canadian Air Member Aeronautical Engineering (AMAE) by the Air Member for Supply (AMS): *'May one of the Boeing 247-D at present at AOS* (Air Observer School) *be allotted to Flight Research Establishment? This aircraft, while not suitable for Observer Training, is of a very desirable type for certain operations in view at Flight Research, as well as for general use there'.*

AMS responded by asking the Air Member for Training (AMT): *'Please advise if you concur in the allotment of 7636 from No. 1 TC to HWE Flight Research Est.'* (The RCAF operated within three broad areas - Home War Establishment (HWE), responsible for the defence of Canada; RCAF Overseas, covering those units and personnel operating within the RAF; and the BCATP. The use of the term HWE in this note was just a way of emphasizing that the aircraft was being transferred from the BCATP).

This correspondence confirms that urgent consideration was being given to fitting 10 cm radar, in a 247-D, as early as November 1940, less than three months after the arrival of Bowen in Canada. This is contrary to the impression given by Bowen in his book 'Radar Days', no doubt unintentionally, that the decision to fit out the Boeing as a flying demonstrator for 10 cm radar was made fairly late on, in the spring of 1941, after the trials on the B-18 at Boston, and after it became evident that a Douglas Boston (Havoc) was not available or was unsuitable for the purpose.[33]

Initially, the request to transfer a Boeing from training use to experimental work was resisted. A message from AMT to AMS dated 25th November 1940 stated: *'This Division cannot approve the release of any Boeings until sufficient Ansons are available to equip all Air Observer Schools now open or opening up to their full establishment. Furthermore it is anticipated that when the Boeings are released from AOSs one will be required at each SFTS engaged in training pupils on single engine aircraft'.*

To this however, the Chief of Air Staff (CAS) crisply responded: *'The work for which AMAE requires the Boeing is of the utmost importance. Please make an aircraft available at Ottawa a.s.a.p. CAS 30.11.40'.*

Already, the urgency of this request had been underlined by a message on 23rd November, from CAS to No. 12 Technical Detachment (TD) : *'It is requested that measurements be taken on a Boeing 247-D at Malton to determine the contour of the portion of fuselage forward of the plane of the propellers'.*

It was important to ensure there was sufficient room in the nose mail and parcel compartment for most of the radar equipment associated with the scanner, and so minimise time-consuming modifications to the aircraft.

In the design of the American 10 cm AI radar, the Radiation Laboratory at MIT had decided to adopt a 'helical' scanner, as opposed to the 'spiral' scanner system used by the British on their 10 cm 'AIS' radar, whose development was well advanced on the other side of the Atlantic. It was crucial that the nose could accommodate the 'swept volume' of the scanner - the helical scanning motion of the scanner moved its 29 inch diameter dish through ± 90 degrees in azimuth and up to -10/+20 degrees in elevation. It was also important that there was space for the radar transmitter close to the scanner. Hence the urgent order for measurements to be taken.

Measurements were duly made of the interior nose space of Boeing 247-D 7636, formerly NC13346, at No. 1 Air Observer School (AOS), Malton. Remarkably, the sketch drawings on squared paper made on that occasion have survived.

These plan and elevation drawings of the nose of the Boeing at Malton, from the front bulkhead of the passenger compartment forward, were forwarded by No. 12 TD, accompanied by a message dated 1st December which was annotated '...tracings to be ready for Prof. R H Fowler, NRC, to take on Wednesday'.

The measurements on 7636 having confirmed the suitability of the aircraft for the radar installation, CAS issued a requirement for a Boeing 247-D to be allotted from Training Command to the Test and Development Establishment (TDE) at Rockcliffe.[34] It was decided to allocate 7655, which was at Trenton, rather than 7636 as originally proposed.

On 13th December, 7655 duly arrived at the TDE at Rockcliffe, having been ferried from Trenton by Sqn Ldr Truscott, accompanied by Sgt Crampton and Cpl Michael – the flight lasted 1 hour 30 minutes. Five days later, Truscott accompanied by Flt Lt Middleton

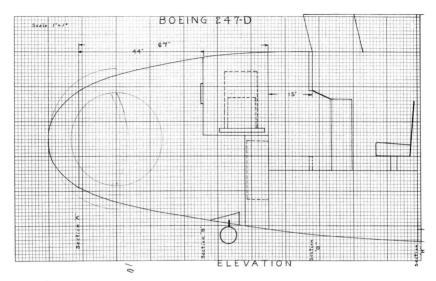

Two of the set of drawings made at Malton in the last week of November 1940

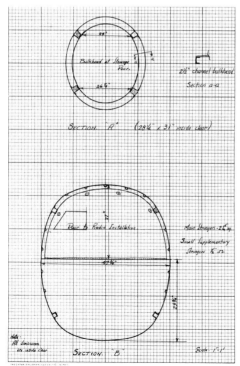

Above, a side elevation of the interior of the nose compartment and forward fuselage of a Boeing 247-D to determine space available for the 10 cm radar with room for the area swept by the motion of its helical scanner.

Left, showing the internal dimensions of cross sections of the interior of the nose compartment of a Boeing 247-D, similarly to determine space available for the scanner for the 10 cm radar.

(Technical drawings © Government of Canada. Reproduced with the permission of the Minister of Public Works and Government Services Canada (2011). Source: Library and Archives Canada)/Department of National Defence fonds/Vol. 5137, file no. 1021-9-122. Via Terry Judge) took 7655 up for a test flight lasting 45 minutes, which no doubt also served to familiarise another pilot with the aircraft. Meanwhile, during that week ending 18th December, Operation Order D/20/40 (Secret) was issued to cover testing of the AI radar in the Boeing.

For an airborne radar to be able to function it must be able to transmit and receive signals through the part of the aircraft structure within which it is installed. In the Boeing, the radar was to be installed in the nose, with the requirement that it could 'look' through the forward hemisphere; therefore it was necessary to develop a 'radio-transparent' nose for the aircraft – and the new nose must be as aerodynamically robust as metal. Without the first-hand experience of constructing 'radomes' available in Britain, this was a considerable challenge for the Canadians, who sought their own solution.

At Rockcliffe, after an inspection of the Boeing by Dr Bowen on 4th January 1941, a start was made cutting off the metal nose in preparation for the fitting of a 'plastic' nose. It appears the term 'plastic' was used to describe moulded plywood bonded with a synthetic resin. This combination of materials was adopted, of course, to offer radio-transparency – elsewhere in the correspondence between NRC and NDRC it is described as a 'plastic wooden nose section'. The new nose would follow the external profile of the nose of a 247-D, forming a large detachable structure which would give much better access than the small nose hatch normally fitted. By late January, the work to remove the metal nose had been completed, and a scanner ('spinner') built by the Sperry Gyroscope Company, was ready in the United States. The scanner was shipped to Rockcliffe so that engineering of the new nose and the installation of the scanner could be completed.

Another part of the NRC, the Division of Mechanical Engineering, headed by J H Parkin, was tasked with development and construction of the new nose. At the beginning of the war this division instituted a programme to develop and encourage the use of wood (particularly plywood) in aircraft construction. Since there was an absence of wood design data applicable to modern aircraft structures, it was decided to undertake the design of a prototype wooden aircraft and, in conjunction with this, to conduct a test programme to provide relevant data. The Department of National Defence and the Department of Munitions and Supply suggested that a moulded plywood Anson wing would be a good project, and work on this began immediately. The 'Wooden Aircraft Project' was headed by Wilfred T Reid who had been involved in the design of the Canadian Vickers Vedette flying-boat, as well as the Rambler light plane. He was ably assisted by R D Hiscocks. With this background, the Structures Laboratory was viewed as having the capability to design and construct a robust radio-transparent moulded plywood nose for the Boeing.

The next order of business was to establish the availability of spares for the aircraft, and ensure there were no interruptions or delays in the anticipated flying programme. On 5th February 1941, AMAE cabled AMS: *'The Boeing 247-D which has been allotted to T&DE is engaged in experimental work of the highest importance. In order to anticipate action which may be necessitated by engine failure, may it be advised, please, if spare engines are readily available for this aircraft?'* The response indicated that there were three spare Wasp S1H1-G engines ordered, but not specifically for 7655. Oddly enough, however, there is no evidence that one or more spare engines followed the Boeing when it went to Britain. It appears the engines of 7655 with which it arrived from the United States, were not changed while it was in Canada.

Going back to 9th August 1940 at Cheyenne, Wyoming, the Aircraft Inspection Report and the Bill of Sale show that when NC13344 left Inland Air Lines it was fitted with Wasp S1H1-G engines serials (left) 5895 and (right) 5779, with Hamilton Standard Controllable Pitch Propellers model 50039AB, serials (left) 22845 and (right) 24161, the engines being near zero-time since overhaul. When the Boeing arrived in Britain, the serial numbers of the engines were recorded as 5315 and 5316, and propellers 279505 and 279506. The RCAF assigned its own inventory numbers to all its engines, and for the Wasp S1H1-G these were 5118 to 5129 and 5315 to 5320, a total of 18 numbers. With eight Boeing 247-D aircraft on charge these inventory numbers cover their 16 engines plus two (not three) spares. Thanks to documents on the Canadian Department of Transport civil registration files, it is possible to achieve a tie-up between the manufacturer's serial numbers and the RCAF inventory number for 16 of these engines. By a process of elimination, this confirms that Pratt & Whitney engines 5779 and 5895 fitted to this Boeing, became RCAF 5315 and 5316.[35] So in all probability the engines installed at Cheyenne in July 1940 remained on the aircraft, identified by the numbers given in Canada as 5315 and 5316 until, as DZ203, it was rebuilt with new R-1340-AN1 engines in 1944.

During early 1941, ideas on radar co-operation and flight testing were evolving. As previously mentioned, it had been planned to test the new 10 cm AI radar, concurrently in the United States and Canada. However, rather than sending the AI radar to Rockcliffe for installation and testing in the Boeing, it was now suggested that once the 'plastic' nose and the scanner had been installed, the aircraft be sent to Boston for completion of the radar installation. It would stay there for about a month, acting as a second laboratory plane to the Douglas B-18, after which it would return to Canada for further flight trials of the radar. Then, after another month or so, it would return to Boston for installation of an AI set which would include the latest improvements.

While waiting for the new 'plastic' nose, considerable work was necessary to build and install a suitable mounting bench for the equipment that was to be installed in the cabin when the Boeing was sent to Boston.

Meanwhile, ground bench-testing of the 10 cm AI radar (now named 'AI-10') was proceeding under the auspices of the Radiation Laboratory. By early February the first prototype of AI-10 was available for fitting to a Douglas B-18 trials aircraft, although hard work over several weeks was still needed before successful airborne results were obtained. The B-18 in question, 37-477, was one of the first of a dozen or more B-18 aircraft which passed through the hands of MIT in 1941 and 1942, most of them for fitting with radar for operational use over the American Atlantic seaboard, seeking U-boats.

A sister aircraft to 7655, this RCAF Boeing 247-D number 7635, shows the appearance and finish of a Boeing 247-D in RCAF service. This particular aircraft, built from scratch as a 247-D, was ordered by Lufthansa but not delivered. In Canada, it was flown by 121 Composite Squadron and is here seen over the RCAF Station at Dartmouth, Nova Scotia. (The Boeing Company)

In Canada, work to accommodate the helical scanner of the US 10 cm radar in the nose of the Boeing was well advanced, and it is worth at this point explaining the scanner system involved. The complete scanner assembly of AI-10 comprised the circular parabolic reflector (or 'mirror') formed from thin aluminium alloy sheet, the radar aerial (a small dipole) fixed at the focal centre of the reflector, and a mechanical drive mechanism, powered by an electric motor driving through a gearbox, to provide the scanning motion for the reflector and aerial system. To achieve a helical scanning motion, required movement of the reflector and aerial in both the horizontal and vertical plane. Up and down tilting movement of the reflector and aerial combination was achieved by mounting it in a yoke so that it could move, between pre-determined limits, about its horizontal axis. Vertical plane movement was achieved by attaching the yoke to a vertical shaft which was spun continuously at 160 rpm whilst the radar was switched on. With each revolution of the shaft, the elevation of the reflector and aerial was incrementally and automatically tilted upwards until it reached the upper elevation limit. On reaching this limit, the reflector/aerial returned to the lower elevation limit, and the cycle repeated continuously.

At the heart of the transmitter (mounted close to the scanner) lay the magnetron. Electrical power applied, via electrical circuitry, to the magnetron enabled it to generate powerful 10 cm microwaves, and further circuitry switched the magnetron off and on several hundred times a second to provide very short pulses of microwave energy. A special type of electrical cable fed the pulse chain from the transmitter to the aerial from which the pulses were radiated onto the reflector. The shape of the reflector focused the pulses into a narrow, powerful, beam of microwave energy and then reflected it forward into space. The two-dimensional motion imparted on the reflector/aerial system, swept the beam in a helical motion through a defined space in front of the aircraft. In order not to expose the crew to high doses of RF radiation, the transmitter switched off when the dish was facing the crew, that is, during the rearward 180 degrees of the arc swept.[36]

By March 1941 events in Canada started to accelerate. In a letter dated 11th March to Mackenzie at NRC, Fowler suggested that after the installation of the radar, the Boeing should remain at Boston for an indefinite period, as it was thought that more rapid progress could be made with both trials aircraft available at the same location. This idea was taken up with AVM Stedman who agreed to the change in plans. At this point the NRC's Radio Section dropped out of the AI programme and moved on to Gun Laying (GL) radar, and other radar projects.

Work on the 'plastic' nose for the Boeing had now reached the stage where on 7th March, it was 'cooked' in an oven, six feet long by four feet wide.[37] The team was still at an early point on the learning curve, and difficulties were encountered when removing the nose from the mould, so it had to be cooked a second time, on 17th March. In the manufacture of the new nose, it seems likely that the removed metal nose section was used as a male mould, or as a former for a female mould. Shortly after, W T Reid of the NRC sent a message to the DND on 21st March 1941, saying: *'We are forwarding tomorrow to T&D, Rockcliffe, one moulded wood nose for the Boeing. This nose is complete with secondary attachment fittings and bolts, but the necessary primary attachments to the main fuselage stringers are to be made by T&D.'*

A note from J H Parkin dated 22nd March says: *'You may be interested to learn that we have just completed the first nose for the Boeing, for the ASV (sic) work. We produced it in one piece instead of in halves as Vidal does. Of course the blister at the bottom was added as a separate piece. I am rather pleased with the result and think that it compares very favorably with Vidal's effort. It will be shipped to the Rockcliffe Air Station almost immediately to be fitted to the aircraft. In the meantime, we are proceeding with the construction of a second, making use of the experience gained in moulding the first one'.*[38] Vidal was a commercially-developed process, similar in principle to that used by NRC in that it involved hot moulding of formed plywood[39], and would later be used to build the fuselage of the all-Canadian Anson Mark V.

The reference to the blister under the nose is interesting, as this was the one obvious external feature which gave evidence of the radar installation in the Boeing, and can be seen in photographs of the aircraft taken during 1941. This 'blister' was a fairing to cover the otherwise protruding scanner drive assembly comprising bearing, motor, gearbox and electrical connections for the scanner.

On 3rd April 1941, a new mounting ring for the moulded nose was fitted to the airframe of the Boeing, followed on 6th April by the fitting and finishing of the nose itself. The Boeing was now ready to be sent to Boston Airport for the AI-10 to be installed. In preparation for this, the British Air Attaché in Washington had cabled RCAF HQ on 5th April to say the American authorities had granted approval for 7655 to visit Boston Municipal Airport, and also for a flight test at the airport (which was renamed Logan Field in 1943).

It is unfortunate that the date of the first flight of 7655 with the new nose is not known, as the daily flying sheets, maintained by T&DE since its inception, were discontinued on 1st April 1941. However, when the Boeing was inspected at Boston on 13th June it was reported

Boeing 247-D c/n 1726 as serial number 7655 of the Royal Canadian Air Force, probably taken in April 1941 shortly before it left Rockcliffe for Boston. The aircraft has already been fitted with the new moulded plywood nose to accommodate the scanner for the 10 cm radar. The bulge under the nose to house the drive for the scanner can be seen. But the aircraft has not yet been painted as DZ203 in RAF camouflage and markings. The propellers still have striped tips to the blades, as seen in US airline service. (Peter M Bowers Collection, The Museum of Flight)

that it had been there 'for approximately ten weeks' which would place its departure from Ottawa at around the end of the first week of April.

However, predictions for the readiness of the 10 cm AI sets for installation in both aircraft continued to be over-optimistic, and in fact, the Douglas B-18 had only made its first flight with this equipment on 27th March.[40] From correspondence on file, it appears the AI installation in the Boeing was not completed until early in May, and was partly delayed because of problems in obtaining some unspecified 'service equipment'.

Further essential engineering modifications on the Boeing concerned its electrical system. There was not sufficient surplus electrical power available from its two engine-driven generators to operate the radar.

Douglas B-18, serial 37-477, modified by the Radiation Laboratory at MIT, was used for the first airborne test of AI-10 radar in March 1941, with the scanner for the 10 cm radar mounted on the nose. This B-18 continued to be used for radar research by MIT, and is here seen in 1942, now on trials of AGL-1 radar, with a scanner in a transparent acrylic 'radome'. AGL-1 was planned for the Douglas A-26A night fighter version of the Douglas Invader. In the event, the Northrop P-61 night fighter fitted with SCR-520 AI radar was preferred, and the A-26A version was discontinued. AGL-1 radar was a adapted from SCR-584 ground-based fire control radar system, which like SCR-520 in the P-61 and a whole family of 10 cm radars stemming from MIT, was based on the British cavity resonant magnetron, and the continuing involvement in the United States of Dr E.G. 'Taffy' Bowen[41]. (Courtesy of the MIT Museum).

The problem was solved by installing a separate petrol engine driven auxiliary power unit (APU) that delivered a great deal of power at 28V DC. The APU was fitted in the compartment space previously occupied by the toilet.

Air Chief Marshal Sir Hugh Dowding, the victor of the Battle of Britain, and who before the war had been an early advocate of AI radar development, was now on a tour of American military establishments. On 29th April 1941, he visited the Radiation Laboratory at MIT to see the developments in 10 cm AI. He was given a flying demonstration in the B-18 thus fitted, actually using the

Boeing 247-D 7655 as a target, and was suitably impressed. As an outcome of this visit, Dowding urged that Britain be supplied with American 10 cm AI sets, to evaluate under more realistic conditions. Bowen wrote in his autobiography: *'There was now great pressure on getting a working model* (of the AI-10 radar) *over to Britain at an early date. It seemed to me the best way of taking the first set to Britain was to install it in an aircraft at Boston, do all the test flying there and take the finished installation over to England in one unit'.*

Having abandoned the idea of fitting AI-10 to a Douglas Boston aircraft, further discussions were held with the Canadians, which in early June resulted in an offer by them to give up their Boeing 247-D, to be dispatched to Britain, together with the American 10 cm AI radar with which it was fitted, and which had been intended for Canada. It was expected that the Boeing could be released for shipment around 10th June.

It is not strictly true to say that the Boeing was a 'gift' from Canada to Britain (as suggested by some sources), in that the aircraft having been paid for by Britain, was already British property. However, by surrendering the Boeing (and with it, the installed radar which had been allocated to Canada) to Britain at this point, the Canadians set back their own radar programme by many months. So their altruistic action by any other criteria can be regarded a gift, and a valuable one at that.

The radar fitted to the Boeing was one of the five prototypes built by the Radiation Laboratory, and incorporated the outcome of the B-18 trials. These early models, being hand-built, no doubt differed from one to another in detail as the design was improved, but were referred to generically as AI-10 (not to be confused with the later AI Mk X).

At the outset, the intention was that one of these five sets would be allocated to Britain for evaluation, and this was now represented by the radar in the Boeing. The second was that installed in the B-18. A third was allocated to Canada to replace that sent to Britain in the Boeing, and would be installed in a Bolingbroke (a Mark IVW, number 9010, one of only 14 Bolingbrokes fitted with Twin Wasp Junior engines). The last two of the five AI-10 sets went to Bell

Bolingbroke IVW 9010 fitted with 10 cm AI radar. This aircraft replaced Boeing 247-D 7655 as a demonstrator of the US AI-10 radar with the RCAF. During 1942, Bolingbroke 9010 was used for 10 cm ASV trials, and later as a radar trainer aircraft with the RCAF. This rare colour photo from Carl Vincent.

Telephone and Western Electric as patterns for production purposes. The British Air Commission in Washington had already ordered ten sets from Western Electric's first production batch.

It was also agreed with NDRC in Washington and NRC in Ottawa, that in support of the flying demonstrator, each country would send one technician to Britain. Bowen had specifically asked that Dr Dale Corson, the American scientist assigned by the Radiation Laboratory to the project and who was responsible for the installation, and Jack (J T) Heath from the Canadian NRC, both of whom were involved in the trials of the Boeing at Boston, accompany him and the Boeing to Britain.

The Boeing with the moulded wood nose installed was inspected at Boston on 13th June 1941 by R D Hiscocks and by the aircraft's pilot, Sqn Ldr Briggs.[42] At the time of this inspection, it was recorded that the aircraft had flown some 40 hours over the ten weeks while at Boston. It is assumed that this inspection was made while the aircraft was being stripped of its AI radar equipment preparatory to its shipment to the UK.

The 247-D was flown from Boston, to Newark Airport, New Jersey (presumably before 18th June which is the date when the pilot, Sqn Ldr Briggs, arrived back in Ottawa), where it was 'cocooned' in preparation for the Atlantic crossing. It was shipped out of Hoboken, New Jersey, aboard a merchantman, in the form of deck cargo as was customary at the time. It is presumed that this ship joined a trans-Atlantic convoy, since a solo voyage would have been very hazardous. Convoy records indicate that it was probably one of more than 40 merchantmen that formed HX138 which left Halifax, Nova Scotia, on 11th July and arrived at Liverpool on 27th July.[43] In order to join this convoy the ship, with the Boeing on deck, must have left Hoboken around 7th July.

Bowen and Corson flew to Britain in a Liberator of the North Atlantic Ferry service on 28th June 1941. Heath travelled separately to Britain at some point in July, possibly within a day or two of Bowen and Corson, though the date is not known. Because the AI-10 for Britain had been first assigned to Canada, Heath was tasked with accompanying the equipment, which weighed about 300 lb, on its journey to Britain. Originally, Heath and his 'extremely secret equipment' were to have left Boston around 17th June by train for Montreal, where the Customs officials had been briefed about his arrival. However, he was unable to get away at that time and, instead, flew up to Montreal around 25th June. From there, Heath (and the AI-10) continued to Britain on a North Atlantic Ferry flight, landing at Prestwick in south west Scotland. On arrival, he arranged delivery of the AI-10 to TFU at Christchurch for unpacking, inspection and testing. Heath later travelled to Liverpool in time to be at Speke aerodrome to see the reassembled Boeing ready for flight testing on 1st August 1941.

Boeing 247-D 7655 was formally 'Struck Off Charge' by the RCAF on 1st July 1941. Sadly, her pilot, Sqn Ldr F E R Briggs, was killed less than three months later. On 13th September, Briggs and Flt Lt W Richards were detailed to perform diving tests in Cessna Crane 7919. They took-off at 11:10 and crashed at 12:00, four miles southeast of Uplands Airport, Ottawa.[44]

6. THE BOEING IN BRITAIN

When Bowen left for North America with the Tizard Mission in August 1940, work to develop AI radar operating in the centimetre waveband, was gathering pace in Britain, as the limitations of the 1.5 metre wavelength AI radar now coming into use with the RAF were already becoming increasingly evident.

At 1.5 metre wavelength, the practical size limits of the radar aerials which could be used meant that the aerials had very wide 'beam widths' (i.e. the angles through which the aerials 'looked'). Whilst the objective of AI was to search for enemy aircraft in the forward hemisphere, 1.5 metre radars also unavoidably saw a great deal of the ground, or sea, over which the aircraft was flying. The radar operator viewed the radar's detections on two CRTs – one for range/amplitude, and another for range/elevation. The size ('amplitude') of the ground signals ('returns') was very large and extensive, and many times greater than any target returns. As long as the range to a target was less than the height at which an AI-fitted fighter was flying (i.e. the range to the ground), then the target might be seen by the operator.

There was an urgent need for an AI radar to operate at lower altitudes, especially close to the sea in order to detect low-flying enemy aircraft, such as mine-layers. Bowen had theorised in 1939 that this could be achieved by utilising very short wavelengths (which became known as microwaves) focused into a narrow beam. He reasoned that focusing could be achieved by fixing the very small aerial required for these wavelengths at the centre of a parabolic reflector ('dish'). The larger the diameter of the dish (the 'aerial aperture'), the narrower the beam, but the size of the space available in the nose of a night fighter was the limiting factor. A diameter of about 30 inches looked possible, and he calculated that with an operating wavelength of 10 cm, a beam width of 10 degrees could be achieved. Having such a narrow beam meant that it would also be necessary to develop a mechanical means of moving it about ('scanning'), in a pre-determined pattern, so that it covered a desired area in front of the aircraft.[45]

A set of air-to-air photographs of the newly-arrived Boeing was taken, up from Boscombe Down, in August 1941, mainly for aircraft recognition purposes, using a Hampden as the camera aircraft. In the photo above, the window in the starboard cabin entrance door can be seen, together with a notice pasted on the inside of the window. A window in the passenger door was an unusual feature in a 247-D but not unique to DZ203. (The Boeing Company)

There were formidable obstacles to be overcome in achieving this. It needed the invention of the resonant cavity magnetron, and it needed an intensive programme of research by the Centimetre Wavelength Group which had been set up at the Telecommunications Research Establishment (TRE) at Worth Matravers, to produce the first 10 cm wavelength AI radar. This set was fitted in the nose of Blenheim N3522 in December 1940, the first successful flight trials taking place in March 1941.[46] This type of radar was referred to at TRE as AIS, with 'AI' standing for Airborne Interception, while the 'S' was stated by some sources to stand for 'Sentimetric' (sic) which seems a little unlikely. A more satisfying explanation is that it referred to S-band wavelengths, nominally 7.5 to 15 cm, as opposed to the 1.5 metre wavelength of AI radar being used at that time.

Trials with AIS in the Blenheim also included successful experiments with the 10 cm wavelength radar in the Air to Surface Vessel (ASV) mode in April 1941. As these flight trials progressed, it also became apparent to the flight observers that the new wavelength would also be useful in the role of ground mapping, that is observing features on the ground which could not be seen at night or through cloud, so assisting bomber aircraft in navigation and finding a target. By the time Bowen returned from America with the Boeing and its US AI-10 radar in July 1941, four Beaufighters were being fitted with the first production British 10 cm AIS sets, which became AI Mk VII.

Among the main objectives in bringing the Boeing and its AI-10 radar to Britain, was the evaluation of the American 10 cm radar with its helical scanner, against the British AI Mk VII with its spiral-pattern scanning motion (TRE had tested a helical scanner for AIS, but opted for spiral scan for AI Mk VII). An outcome would be a statement of the operational requirements so that American production of 10 cm AI could start in a form suitable for combat use, which would meet British requirements.[47]

The Boeing arrived by sea at Liverpool on 27th July 1941, and docked on the 28th. The aircraft was unloaded on the 29th, and transported to Speke aerodrome, where it was assembled by the Lockheed British Reassembly Division.[48] Having been allocated the RAF serial number DZ203, it was recorded as being at Speke on 2nd August *'Delivery after shipment from USA'*.

Immediately on landing in Britain four weeks earlier, Bowen had travelled to TRE at Worth Matravers, where he and Corson were later joined by Heath. The American 10 cm AI and the British equivalent were set up on a bench side-by-side for comparative testing. It was concluded that although the American set was better engineered, the two sets gave comparable results. The American set could put out significantly more power, but the British set could pick up signals that were several times fainter. It was decided to connect the British receiver to the American scanner. This combination immediately picked up a target three times further away. It did not take long to identify that the silicon diode crystals in the British receiver were the

In these pictures from the set of air-to-air photos of DZ203, note the wavy demarcation line between upper and lower surfaces, and the irregular execution of this on starboard rear fuselage. (Crown copyright)

main factor in this improvement. The Americans had, at the start of their development work, also used solid state diodes but had dropped them in favour of vacuum tubes. The results of these comparative tests heralded an upsurge in crystal research by the Americans, with far reaching consequences.[49]

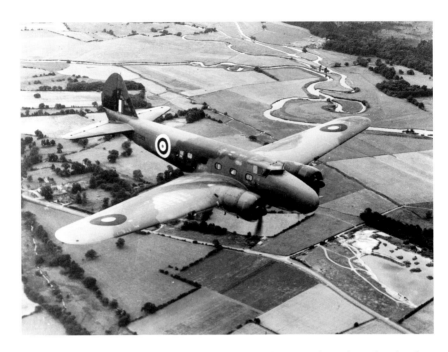

In this and other photos in the set of air-to-air photographs, taken shortly after the arrival of the Boeing in Britain, note the scuffing of the paint on the top of the fuselage, fin and inner wing surfaces, probably caused during the voyage across the Atlantic as deck cargo. (The Boeing Company)

Meanwhile, preparations were put in hand for the Boeing to be taken on strength by the TRE's flight trials unit, then known as the Special Duty Flight (SDF) but soon to be re-named the TFU, at Christchurch, and demonstrated as soon as it was available. On 31st July, the ORB (Operations Record Book) of the Fighter Interception Unit (FIU) at Ford in Sussex, recorded: *'Dr Bowen came from TRE to make arrangements for FIU to test the new 10 cm AI which has been developed in America and is installed in a Boeing 247-D'.* Bowen would have been aware that it was important to test the Boeing with its American 10 cm AI radar not only at Christchurch, but also in front of wide and critical audiences at the main aviation centres for research and development, starting with the scientists of TRE, and most importantly, the Fighter Interception Unit (FIU) at Ford, which

Boeing 247-D DZ203 in England, 1941. (Crown copyright)

had recently pioneered and proved the operational use of 1.5 metre AI radar in night fighters. The FIU was established in April 1940 under the direction of Fighter Command, charged with the operational testing and evaluation of AI radar equipment. FIU proved to be so effective in its role that the first 'kills' with several marks of AI radar were achieved whilst in their hands for evaluation. Having been based initially at Tangmere, FIU moved to Ford in January 1941. The Boeing with its American radar, also needed to be shown to the Royal Aircraft Establishment (RAE) at Farnborough, and the Aeroplane and Armament Experimental Establishment (A&AEE) at Boscombe Down.

A young pilot of the SDF was sent from Christchurch to Speke to test fly the Boeing, and assuming all was well, deliver it, firstly to Boscombe Down. This pilot was Flt Lt Frank Griffiths, who was to play a continuing part in the story of DZ203 in radar research.

It is appropriate that Griffiths was the first member of the RAF to pilot the Boeing in Britain, since he was also one of the last to fly it, more than five years later, after playing a leading role in the advances in radar-assisted automatic landing made by this aircraft.

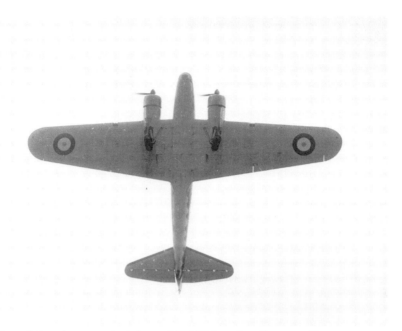

Another of the photographs taken of DZ203 for aircraft recognition purposes, showing the plan view. (The Boeing Company)

On 1st August 1941, Griffiths duly flew to Speke in Blenheim Z5909, accompanied by Fg Off Wright, who flew the Blenheim back to Christchurch. Griffiths met Jack Heath who was waiting for him at Speke and on 2nd August, Griffiths accompanied by Heath, flew the Boeing on a brief air test, landing back at Speke after 35 minutes. All was evidently satisfactory, as Griffiths with Heath as a passenger, flew the aircraft directly from Speke to Boscombe Down, the flight lasting 1 hour 10 minutes. The stay at Boscombe Down was brief, presumably to explore the Boeing's handling qualities, with landing and take-off tests being carried out by Sqn Ldr Macguire alongside Griffiths. These tests involved just 35 minutes flying time, then the Boeing was on its way again, Griffiths and Heath finishing the day at Christchurch, after a 20 minute hop from Boscombe Down. The following day, 3rd August, the Boeing was at Farnborough, but by the 5th, it was back at Christchurch where the scientists of TRE had more opportunity to get to know the aircraft and try out its radar.

Frank Griffiths in 1941 – in the cockpit of a Douglas Havoc night fighter[50] at Christchurch. (Douglas Fisher Collection)

Reg Batt in his memoirs[51] of radar development at TRE and TFU, records the scene of the arrival of the Boeing at Christchurch as follows: *'... by 1941, applications of centimetre technique began to proliferate ... (there) came two well-dressed gentlemen with a large van-load of equipment packed in crates ... both had American accents. Heath and Corsen (sic), who were to spend about six months with us, were from the new Radiation Laboratory of Massachusetts Institute of Technology, set up following the Tizard Mission to North America. In hardly six months of its existence the laboratory produced a version of centimetre AI system to a program negotiated by Bowen and using British-inspired 10 centimetre components. This version was to use the more straightforward helical scanner, but it required a twin cathode-ray tube display to impart the three parameters of range, azimuth and elevation ... in three packing cases were the results of MIT's work with which Heath and Corsen (and a twin-engined aircraft in which to fly the system) had faced the hazards of an Atlantic convoy in order that comparative tests could be made with our own system ... The aircraft which had been shipped over and given into the caring hands of the TFU at Christchurch was a twin-engined commercial airliner – a Boeing 247-D'.*

Reg Batt went on to describe the interior of the Boeing soon after its arrival from America: *'The accommodation was first-class (as was passenger flight before the war), for down each side of the cabin was a row of comfortable seats like armchairs. There would have been a total of about 16 of these* (actually ten), *but all along one side the seats had been removed and in their place fitted a long bench with numerous power supplies (115 volts, 400 hertz) for the radar equipment. In addition, there were 24-volt DC sockets for the* (American) *low-voltage soldering irons. This really impressed us for such irons had not been seen in Britain at that time. With all these unique facilities the aircraft was a veritable flying laboratory in which repairs and modifications could be made in flight. When Heath and Corsen* (sic) *returned to America they took only key items of their equipment. Our group found their tools and spares very welcome, but the star prize was the Boeing aircraft. Henceforth, the group were the*

Another photo taken during the air-to-air sortie from Boscombe Down, but not included in the set of photos subsequently issued 'for Official use'.(The Boeing Company)

enviable possessors of this remarkable and comfortable flying lab which was invaluable for flight testing a whole variety of experimental equipment'.

On 5th August, Griffiths took the Boeing up for a 55 minute flight which is recorded as 'experimental', with four other persons on board (it is highly likely that three of them were Bowen, Heath and Corson). Initial trials were disappointing. Heath wrote on 7th August from Christchurch to Dr J T Henderson at NRC:

'We have at last got our plane, and made a flight with the equipment. The ship arrived at Liverpool on Monday July 28th. The plane was taken off the ship on a floating crane Tuesday noon, and was able to fly to Christchurch Saturday afternoon August 2nd. We installed the equipment on Sunday afternoon, but due to difficulties with the plane itself, and with the target planes, we have only had one flight on which we could see the target plane. At that time we had to "wash out" the flight, as the target was flying at 7500 feet, and we had no permission to fly over 5000 feet, and were therefore in danger of being shot down'.[52]

However, these were very early days, and later results would be much more impressive.

Griffiths did not fly the Boeing himself for the next eight days, but no doubt it was being tried and tested by other pilots of the SDF. On 13th August, Griffiths took up Flt Sgt Berryman as second pilot, to convert him to type.

On 13th August, Christchurch had a distinguished visitor in the person of Sir Henry Tizard, whose drive and inspiration had initiated the co-operation with the United States and Canada that resulted in the arrival of the Boeing with its American built 10 cm radar in Britain. It must have been a source of great satisfaction to him to see at first-hand what had been achieved.

Bowen hoped to demonstrate the 10 cm radar in the Boeing to Sir Henry, who was accompanied by Professor John Cockcroft (who had also been a member of the Tizard Mission) and Dr Philip Dee from TRE. Bad weather prevented the flight from going ahead, but they were shown a *'good simulation of the results with a target going round and around the aerodrome'*.[53] The author Peter Moss stated (although his source is not known) that on this date there was a demonstration to Sir Henry Tizard at Christchurch of the application of radar to blind bombing *'... with the aid of American 10 cm radar from the Boeing'*.[54] Perhaps this was the intention, but the weather dictated otherwise. The interest of Sir Henry in 'blind bombing' showed the shape of things to come, although at the time the 10 cm radar fitted was regarded as essentially for Airborne Interception (AI).

On 14th August, the day after Tizard's visit, the 247-D flew from Christchurch to the FIU at Ford for intensive trials, piloted by Frank Griffiths and accompanied by five passengers, including Bowen. On arrival at Ford, Griffiths converted several FIU pilots to type, by flying dual with them on the Boeing. The FIU pilots included the renowned Flt Lt Glyn 'Jumbo' Ashfield (who had been the first pilot to shoot down an enemy aircraft at night using AI radar, on 22nd July 1940), and the CO of the FIU, Wg Cdr Evans, who later became the Station Commander at Defford in 1946. He retired in 1970 as Air Chief Marshal Sir Donald Randell Evans KBE, CB, DFC.

The ORB of FIU Ford recorded: *'Under the aegis of Dr Bowen of TRE, and Mr Heath and Mr Corson of Canada* (sic), *a Boeing 247-D appeared, equipped with American 10 cm AI. The Commanding Officer and Flt Lt Ashfield went solo on it forthwith, that is solo with about a dozen advisors each. They also did some tests of the 10 cm'*.[55]

The following day, *'Practically everyone flew in the Boeing, while it had its 10 cm AI tested'*. This included a flight with Ashfield and Evans at the controls, accompanied by their fellow FIU pilots, Sqn Ldr Hiscox and Fg Off Randall, together with Dr Corson and Mr Heath, lasting 1 hour 25 minutes. The next day, Flt Lt Ashfield did some more flying in the Boeing, during which Sqn Ldr Hiscox tried out the 10 cm AI. Evans then piloted the Boeing, accompanied by Dr Bowen and Sqn Ldr Hiscox, for a demonstration to Air Cdre Elliot, Wg Cdr Pearson and Sqn Ldr Adams of Headquarters, Fighter Command. Finally on 17th August 1941, *'F/Lt Ashfield and numerous others flew in the Boeing, while expert observers – including S/Ldr Adams – examined the 10 cm AI. Sir Archibald Sinclair, Bt, CMG,*

MP, Secretary of State for Air, visited the Unit'. After a few further trials, the Boeing returned to Christchurch late the following day.

The FIU report[56] on the outcome of the trials at Ford noted that with the American system as installed in the Boeing, the scanner was driven electrically and the scan motion was helical, in contrast to the hydraulically driven spiral scanner of the British AIS with which FIU were familiar. The presentation showing the position of the target relative to the interceptor aircraft, was on a cathode ray tube (CRT) in the cabin, repeated on a second CRT fixed in the pilot's cockpit. Target aircraft used for the evaluation of AI-10 at Ford over nine hours of flying, included a Beaufighter, a Defiant and a Shark. An echo from a target aircraft appeared on the CRT as a horizontal bright line about half an inch in length. To get an indication of range on the CRT, a switch had to be operated, which meant the direction of the target and the distance to the target could not be read at the same time. The conclusion of FIU was that indications of azimuth and elevation were excellent (although the area swept in elevation was too small), but the inability to read direction and range at the same time was a very serious operational disadvantage. In any case, the range indication was poor and not calibrated, so was of little value operationally. The pilot's CRT was unavoidably fitted in an awkward position, being suspended from the roof of the cockpit. This position, remote from the blind flying instruments, and the lack of any datum lines, made it difficult to read. Despite these handicaps, Flt Lt Ashfield, whilst completely screened from any outside view, did one successful approach up to minimum range on a target.

In conclusion, the report of FIU said that the whole equipment as fitted in the Boeing, was too large and heavy to be installed in a night fighter, but noted that the necessary modifications to reduce bulk and weight were in hand.

Despite the disadvantages, FIU concluded that '*...the equipment showed the greatest promise and would offer a weapon of the highest operational value against the night bomber'*.[57]

The renowned Flt Lt Glyn 'Jumbo' Ashfield (the first pilot to shoot down an enemy aircraft at night, using AI radar, on 23rd July 1940), who tested the new American 10 cm AI radar on DZ203 between 14th and 18th of August 1941, at FIU Ford, soon after the Boeing arrived from North America. (The Douglas Fisher Collection)

Meanwhile, 'Taffy' Bowen returned by ship to Halifax, arriving in Washington on 7th September.[58]

Immediately before returning to Canada and the United States, Bowen made his own summary of the trials with the Boeing for the benefit of Dr Darwin at NRC. He described the four days of trials at FIU, when flights had taken place over land and sea at various heights with a variety of targets. The trials had involved interceptions directed by verbal instructions from AI operator to pilot, and compared this procedure with that of the pilot using his own indicator. They found the former method (which became the norm for the next few years) particularly easy to work, and it was possible to follow targets around tight 180 degree turns. Interceptions on the pilot's indicator were successful but difficult to accomplish because of the poor positioning of the CRT, which Bowen suggested should be alongside the gyro compass and artificial horizon.

When flying at 5,000 feet, the maximum useful range of the AI radar was between 3 and 3½ miles, while the minimum range averaged 400 feet. At lower heights the maximum useful range diminished, but the data was not sufficient to specify the rate at which the decrease took place. At the end of the trials, a report with recommendations was agreed by FIU personnel and TRE, and forwarded to NRC in Canada and NRDC in the United States. After further flights back at Christchurch involving, on successive days from 18th August, Gp Capt Hart, Wg Cdr Pretty and Mr Townsend from Fighter Command, together with, at various times, senior TRE scientists Dee, Skinner, Ratcliffe, Pringle, Taylor and Downing, there had been general agreement with the statement of requirements prepared by FIU.

Bowen concluded his letter by reporting that on 26th August, there were further trials *'before the suggested alterations to our ASV equipment',* this presumably relating to moving on to trials of the AI-10 radar for anti-submarine (ASV) work. He finished by saying *'after about 30 hours in the air, the performance'* (of the 10 cm radar) *'has fallen off and it is doubtful whether it can be maintained in working order so far from MIT'.*[59] With hindsight, Dr Bowen's prognosis seems unduly pessimistic, or perhaps he simply underestimated the ability of the technical staff at Christchurch and Worth Matravers to adapt to the demands of the new centimetre-wavelength technology.

During September 1941, it became increasingly apparent that the moulded wood nose fitted to the Boeing was causing many of the problems. On his return to the United States towards the end of September, Dale Corson reported that in the course of the tests in England, the nose of the Boeing became soaked with water, giving rise to large amounts of scattered radiation, and hence undesirable ground echoes, particularly below a height of 4,000 feet. This was of particular concern to the Canadians who were constructing a similar 'plastic wooden nose' for the Bolingbroke to be used for 10 cm AI trials.[60] In fact, the potential problem of water ingress had been identified while the Boeing was at Boston before shipping to England. The aircraft had been exposed to the weather at Boston Airport for ten weeks, as the Radiation Laboratory was not able to take possession of 6,300 sq ft of hangar space in the National Guard building for its aircraft until July 1941. During its time at Boston, rain had leaked into the moulded plywood nose of the Boeing, causing damage at several points, including peeling paint.[61] Although it had been concluded that the radar nose was sound structurally, it was suggested *'a coat of paint before shipment would considerably improve the appearance'*. The nose was therefore given two coats of cellulose lacquer as a protective finish before leaving Boston.[62]

Back in Canada in early March 1941, when difficulties were experienced in forming the first 'plastic' plywood nose, a second nose incorporating lessons learned, was started on 13th of that month. It was completed on the 21st, to be cooked and then stripped on 28th March. During April, the ring for this nose was completed, and the second nose fitted and sanded. It was then removed and held in reserve. After the inspection of the original nose on 13th June, instructions were issued on 19th June to have the second nose prepared for shipment to RAF Christchurch as a spare. After some delay, the second nose was finished, crated and shipped to the UK on 20th August[63], but there is no record of its arrival.

In the meantime, it was concluded the solution to the problem was to replace 'the plastic wooden nose', (or to use the term which soon became current, 'radome') with one moulded from an acrylic polymer, either British 'Perspex' or American 'Plexiglas', which Bowen had hoped would be fitted before the Boeing left Boston. Dr Henderson of NRC in Canada cabled Bowen suggesting a nose be made in this type of material in Britain, and drawings of the NRC 'special nose' forwarded so this could be done. These drawings were sent on 2nd August 1941.

The flight trials during August 1941 showed there was intense interest in the American 10 cm radar in Britain, and Bowen must have been pleased to demonstrate this very satisfactory outcome of one aspect of the Tizard Mission to the United States. He later commented: *'...when the Tizard Mission arrived in America, the US were well ahead of Britain in receiver design, but had nothing remotely comparable with the British resonant magnetron. By July 1941, the position was exactly reversed. The American 10 cm pulse transmitter in the Boeing 247-D was clearly ahead of its equivalent in Britain, but the British receivers were better'.*

In October 1941, Bowen was back in the United States, where as early as May 1941, the decision had been taken to engineer the AI-10 radar into a model suitable for production by Westinghouse as the SCR-520 model. The British were keenly interested in procurement of this American radar, but it was thought SCR-520 was still too large and heavy to be installed comfortably in a Beaufighter (though the larger American P-61 Black Widow was designed to take it). However, at the time of the demonstrations of the Boeing and its American AI-10 radar in August 1941, the British 10 cm AI radar was showing great promise in the form of AI Mk VII which shortly was to go into limited production. So, while awaiting improvements to SCR-520, the British continued with the development of 10 cm AIS radar into larger scale manufacture of the further improved AI Mk VIII.[64] The first Beaufighter to be fitted with AIS at Christchurch, went in November 1941 to FIU at Ford, where it was intensively flown and tested by Wg Cdr Evans, Flt Lt Ashfield and others. In December, Evans made the first successful night interception of an enemy aircraft with the British 10 cm AI radar, when he located and damaged a Ju88 while on anti-minelayer patrol over the Thames estuary, vindicating the belief in 10 cm AI for low-level interception of enemy aircraft dropping mines by night.[65]

In the meantime, the Boeing had a new home. In August 1941, SDF had amalgamated with other more minor units and been renamed the Telecommunications Flying Unit (TFU), and had moved from the rather unsatisfactory aerodrome at Christchurch, to Hurn airfield. The entry on the Ministry of Aircraft Production (MAP) history card (Form 2101) for DZ203, says on 27th August 1941 *'Despatched from TFU to Cunliffe-Owen by air',* but this is crossed out and replaced with: *'Despatched from Christchurch to Hurn by air'.* A small detachment from TFU remained at Christchurch until 10th November, when the transfer to Hurn was supposed to be complete. Griffiths flew DZ203 to Christchurch from Hurn on 11th November, and this was probably one of the last movements flown by TFU in and out of

Christchurch. Between August and November, it is evident the Boeing spent time at both Christchurch and Hurn. After that, it remained based at Hurn until 23rd May 1942, when it was to fly to TFU's new home at Defford.

Aircraft recognition was of paramount importance to military personnel and civilians alike in wartime Britain. It was clearly essential that an unfamiliar but friendly aircraft flying in the skies of Britain should be recognised as such. Unfortunate tragic incidents involving misidentification of Allied types were all too frequent. For example, in December 1942, a Beaufighter from TFU was taking part in radar trials over the North Sea when it was shot down by Spitfires from Coltishall. This resulted in the death of the distinguished scientist Dr A E Downing which presented a severe setback to the AI Mk IX radar programme.

As well as testing all new types of aircraft, A&AEE at Boscombe Down was charged with taking photographs on the ground and in the air for aircraft recognition purposes[66], and normally did so at the first opportunity. A fine set of air to air photographs of the Boeing 247-D DZ203 were taken from a Hampden, covering all angles. Happily most of these photographs survive, and are reproduced in this chapter.

Subsequently, four of these images were deliberately reduced in resolution to create more of a silhouette effect, and together with accurate three view drawings of DZ203, duly appeared in the official aircraft recognition manual AP1480A, which was the 'bible' for the Royal Observer Corps during the war.[67] The photographs and accurate silhouette drawings (which actually include the 'bump' under the nose associated with the AI-10 scanner) were then circulated to authorised users by the Air Technical Publications Board (ATP) at Chessington.

This dissemination of information must have been effective, as the Boeing sailed serenely across the skies of Britain throughout the war, without any 'friendly fire' incidents remaining on record.

But it is probable that many more people read the independent magazine 'Aeroplane Spotter' than had access to the 'For Official Use Only' AP1480A.

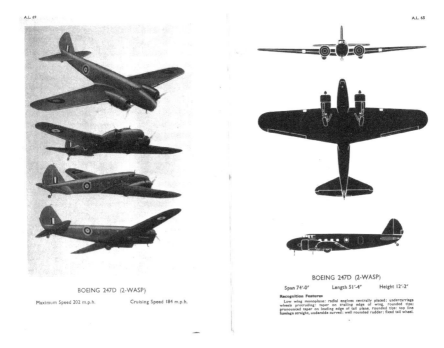

BOEING 247D (2-WASP)

Maximum Speed 202 m.p.h.   Cruising Speed 184 m.p.h.

BOEING 247D (2-WASP)

Span 74'-0"   Length 51'-4"   Height 12'-2"

Recognition Features
Low wing monoplane: radial engines centrally placed; undercarriage wheels protruding; taper on trailing edge of wing, rounded tips; pronounced taper on leading edge of tail plane, rounded tips; top line fuselage straight, underside curved; well rounded rudder; fixed tail wheel.

The entry for the Boeing 247-D in AP1480A, Recognition Handbook of British Aircraft, Ministry of Aircraft Production and The Air Council, pp.65 and 69. This is from the November 1941 edition, but had almost certainly appeared in earlier editions. (Crown copyright via Neville Cullingford, The Royal Observer Corps Museum)

Even by its own standards, the 'Aeroplane Spotter' was exceptionally quick off the mark when, on the 28th August 1941, less than a month after the Boeing 247-D had appeared in Britain, it published a photograph, three-view silhouettes and general information on the type, one of which it said was *'now flying in this country'*.

The 'Aeroplane Spotter' would not yet have had (and in any event would not have been allowed to use), the official photographs and silhouettes, so had to settle for a retouched photograph of the 1934 'MacRobertson Race' 247-D and base its own silhouettes on this aircraft. Unfortunately, these illustrations showed the more

THE BOEING 247-D

AN AMERICAN type of which at least one is now flying in this country is the Boeing 247-D. It is a particularly interesting aeroplane because it was the first modern two-motor low-wing monoplane transport aeroplane and introduced the present design in air liners. The 247 was first produced in 1933 and the 247-D followed in 1934 with several modifications. The Russian CKB-26 bomber was developed from the Boeing Y1B-9A, a military version of the 247. Boeing 247s were used extensively on air lines in the United States until the Douglas DC-2 arrived and three were sold to the German air line company, Deutsche Luft Hansa. They

were the first American high-performance multi-motor commercial aeroplanes to be sold abroad. A Boeing 247-D was flown by Col. Roscoe Turner and Clyde Pangbourne in the MacRobertson Race in 1934 and won third place for speed.

A number of Boeing 247-Ds has been bought from American transport companies by Great Britain and some are in use in Australia and Canada for air crew training.

The Boeing 247 (two 550 h.p. geared supercharged Pratt and Whitney Wasp motors) is a low-wing cantilever monoplane of all-metal construction and light-alloy covering, except for the elevators and rudder, which are fabric covered. Accommodation is for crew of two and 10 passengers.

DIMENSIONS.—Span, 74 ft.; length, 51 ft. 4 ins.; height, 12 ft. 1¾ ins.; wing area, 836.13 sq. ft.; aspect ratio, 6.45.

WEIGHTS.—Empty, 8,940 lb.; loaded, 13,650 lb.

PERFORMANCE.—Max. speed, 202 m.p.h. at 5,000 ft.; range, 800 miles at 184 m.p.h. at 8,000 ft.; initial climb, 1,000 ft. per min.; service ceiling, 21,400 ft.

POINTS OF RECOGNITION.—Low-wing tapered monoplane with all the taper on the trailing edge. Rounded tips. Cylindrical fuselage with long rounded nose. Big single fin and rudder. Radial motors project well forward.

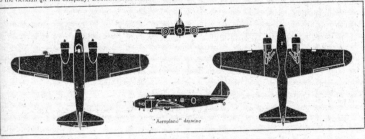

"Aeroplane" drawing

The report on the Boeing 247-D 'now flying in this country' which appeared in The Aeroplane Spotter for 28th August 1941, just four weeks after the aircraft arrived in Britain. As ever at this time of restricted information, there is a fair amount of 'duff gen' in this report (RAF slang for incorrect information). The Russian 'CKB-26'(SB) was not developed from the Y1B-9. No Boeing 247-D served as a crew trainer in Australia. The silhouette and retouched photo are based on the 1934 'MacRobertson' Race runner-up, which had a back sloping windscreen, unlike the forward raked screen of DZ203.

conventional back-sloping windscreen on a late model 247-D, rather than the earlier forward-raked screen retained by DZ203, while of course there was no visual evidence of the very secret radar scanner. But the enterprising 'Aeroplane Spotter' and its silhouettes would have been more than good enough to help identify the sole RAF Boeing as it droned across the sky, and may have done more than AP1480A to save it from 'friendly fire'.

Later in the war, in 1943, the 'Aeroplane Spotter' printed again their silhouettes and photograph of the 247-D, this time altered to show contemporary RAF roundels with narrow white and yellow rings.

A set of 'walk-round' photographs on the ground was also taken of the Boeing in August 1941, very soon after its arrival in Britain, at Christchurch. Four photographs from this set have survived (see Chapter One). These and the A&AEE air-to-air photos clearly show the bulge under the nose associated with the scanner for the AI-10 radar, which was also evident on a photograph of 7655 taken in Canada, after the scanner had been fitted but while the aircraft was still in Canadian colours.

Meanwhile, in the autumn of 1941, the demonstrations to important visitors continued at Hurn. The distinguished scientist Sir Frank Smith, the Director of Telecommunications at the Ministry of Aircraft Production (MAP), inspected AI-10 on October 9th. It was Sir Frank who had arranged with Bowen for the Boeing to be brought to Britain and its AI radar evaluated by FIU. The following week Gp Capt Wansborough and others from various Ministry and military scientific establishments, came to see what was described as the 'American AIS'. Demonstrations emphasised the relevance of 10 cm radar for ASV and night bombing, as well as for AI, and these topics were explored in an ever expanding research and development programme at TRE and TFU.

Towards the end of 1941, the role of the Boeing as a demonstrator of AI-10 had largely been fulfilled. DZ203 was being used increasingly as a light transport and communications aircraft for TRE and TFU personnel, while it awaited a new role.[68]

On 12th November, Frank Griffiths must have had an interesting trip around West Wales in the Boeing, when he flew with five passengers to Manorbier (near Tenby) the home of the obscure Pilotless Aircraft Unit (equipped with Queen Bee biplanes); then on to Carew Cheriton where a flight of Beaufighters charged with the interception of Focke-Wulf Condor shipping raiders was based, together with the Coastal Command Development Unit, who were much interested in ASV; and finishing at the evocatively named Stormy Down where No. 7 Air Gunners School flew Whitleys and Battles on training duties. With hindsight it might be concluded that Griffiths and his colleagues were checking out coastal airfields for their suitability for the ASV trials that were now anticipated for the Boeing.

TRE was already looking beyond 10 cm technology to the next big advance in radar science, which would come from utilisation of even shorter wavelengths, at around 3 cm, in the 'X-band'. By 8th January 1942, it would seem that AI-10 had reached the end of its usefulness, as its scanner had been removed from the Boeing in anticipation of a new 3 cm radar being built by TRE. Whilst work continued in the laboratories and workshops on building the new 3 cm radar at TRE at Worth Matravers, the Boeing was still listed as being used for communications work.

On 24th January 1942, Griffiths had a busy day. In anticipation of the intensive trials with 3 cm radar to come, he made three dual training flights in the Boeing to convert three pilots to type – Sqn Ldr Pippet, Fg Off Frank Brown, and Flt Sgt Christian. He then flew to Northolt with Brown and Flt Lt 'Slogger' Slocombe, returning to Hurn to land in snow. On 4th February, Griffiths was off again in the Boeing accompanied by Slocombe, flying to Cambridge and back.

The Boeing was clearly busy in this period, with more pilots needed for the aircraft. The reason for the activity is confirmed by a TFU report[69] covering the period 16th February to 15th March 1942: *'The Boeing aircraft which was used to demonstrate American AIS, is being adapted for test installations on 3 cm'*. This involved, amongst other things, fitting a new radio-transparent nose, to accommodate the two different scanner reflectors to be evaluated for 3 cm radar. While the new nose was being constructed and fitted, in March and April 1942, two Auxiliary Power Units (APUs) were installed in order to supply extra electrical power required for the new equipment.[70]

To conclude the story of the trials with AI-10 radar in the Boeing, these had far reaching effects. They confirmed the ability of the Americans to design a successful radar, and the results from the trials with the Boeing met their own and British requirements. This led to the production of the SCR-520 radar and then SCR-720, which as AI Mk X from 1943 slowly displaced AI Mk VIII, and became the RAF's standard night fighter radar for the rest of the war and into the 1950s. AI Mk X was a good all-round radar with many positive features, especially superior anti-jamming performance which was important for intruder operations. But above all it was promptly available in large quantities thanks to the overwhelming manufacturing capacity of the United States. With AI Mk X meeting the needs of the RAF for airborne interception, this enabled British industry to develop and manufacture other radars to meet the specific requirements of the British armed forces, in the air, at sea and on the ground. The Tizard Mission which resulted in the trials in Britain with AI-10 in the Boeing, and the positive British feedback from night-fighting experience, had given an enormous boost to the industrial strength of the United States in the interests of winning the Second World War, and succeeded in this beyond all reasonable expectation.[71] In this, as far as radar was concerned, the Boeing 247-D DZ203 had played a key role.

In 1946, the American writer J.P. Baxter[72] said of the magnetron: *'When members of the Tizard Mission brought one to America in 1940, they carried the most valuable cargo ever brought to these shores'.* By early 1942, the prospect of the availability of American 10 cm radar in quantity to Britain went a long way towards repaying that gift, while confirming Tizard's judgement and justifying Winston Churchill's act of faith.

7. A NEW CHALLENGE – EXPLORING THE X-BAND

Towards the end of 1941, the mission of Boeing 247-D DZ203 to demonstrate the American 10 cm (S-band) radar in all its potential applications - AI, ASV and Blind Bombing - was largely complete. Meanwhile, airborne radar development had raced ahead of the Boeing's prototype AI-10 radar fit, with rapid progress being made with radars in the 10 centimetre band in Britain and America. Co-operation between the two countries was now total. After Pearl Harbour, the United States was no longer a benign neutral but a fighting partner, and the Allies benefited as American scientific capability was geared up to the war effort. There would soon be an American presence at TRE Malvern with the establishment of the British Branch of the Radiation Laboratory (BBRL), an outstation of MIT's Radiation Laboratory, this further facilitating the Anglo-American exchange of radar knowledge.

The Boeing had proven itself, with its adaptability, docile flight characteristics and roomy cabin in which scientists and technicians could work, to be an ideal tool for airborne radar research. From the start of 1942, this aircraft had a new and vital mission.

With 10 cm (S-band) radar established, the next challenge was in the even shorter wavelengths, around 3 cm, referred to as the X-band. Working at 3 cm offered a number of advantages, in relation to more compact scanners, sharper beam angles and the opportunity of an extended period of immunity from countermeasures. The downside of this was that the calculated power output for X-band radar would reduce the useful range. Much needed to be done, to explore the benefits and disadvantages of X-band, and turn the potential into fruition.

Applications for X-band were seen in three areas, and the Boeing had to have the flexibility to investigate all of these. First, although 10 cm AI radar was fine for interception of enemy night bombers flying at height or even at reasonably low altitudes, the Royal Navy needed an AI radar which would be effective at yet lower levels, close to the sea. Second, Coastal Command and the Fleet Air Arm demanded better resolution for ASV, and also foresaw the need to keep ahead of the anticipated ability of U-boats to detect first 1.5 metre then 10 cm radar transmissions. Third, although 'blind bombing' by ground mapping (code named H_2S) in the 10 cm band had yet to be used operationally by Bomber Command (and would not be for some time because of fears that a magnetron-based set could fall into enemy hands), further improvements would be needed in terms of resolution and range, resistance to 'jamming', and keeping ahead of further German countermeasures that might emerge.

The Fleet Air Arm was perhaps quickest to seize on the potential of 3 cm radar. A Royal Navy section of TFU which was established at Hurn, was expanded at Defford, and by the end of the war had grown to several hundred personnel. The Navy needed low-level AI radar for the new Firefly fleet fighter, which as a two-seater was seen to have high promise as a night fighter. At the same time, the fitting of 3 cm ASV was envisaged for the new Barracuda carrier-based bomber. However, neither aircraft, even in prototype form, would be available for quite some time, since both were to suffer protracted periods of gestation. The first Barracuda intended to be fitted with any form of ASV was the Mark II, the prototype of which did not fly until August 1942 (in the event, the production Barracuda II would be fitted with 1.5 metre ASV Mk IIN). The night fighter version of the Firefly, the NF Mk II, was even further away. In early 1942, the first prototype Firefly Z1826 had only just had its first flight (on 22nd December 1941), and no production Fireflies of any sort would be made available until 1943.

The narrowness of the 3 cm radar beam was its strength but also a weakness for AI when used against a rapidly manoeuvring target. A report dated 2nd February 1942, by Dr Herbert Skinner of TRE[73], detailed the specification for 3 cm radar for the Firefly. This insisted that because of the ease with which a manoeuvring target once acquired in the narrow beam could then be lost, it was essential to incorporate a 'Lock-Follow' or 'Lock-On' system, development of which had been initiated at TRE in the autumn of 1941. An early example had already been demonstrated by TFU in a Blenheim, in which a 10 cm scanner was designed to search for a target, and when this was found, lock on to it. The concept would now be extended to 3 cm AI radar.

On 23rd May 1942 and the days that followed, all the fifty or more TFU aircraft, including the Boeing, flew from Hurn to Defford, to be joined there by all their equipment and ground crews, while the scientists of TRE settled in at Malvern. Group 8 at TRE had been set up at Worth Matravers with responsibility for 3 cm transmitters, receivers and diodes, and together with Group 9 under Dr John Warren, which was dedicated specifically to 3 cm ASV, moved to Malvern with the rest of the Establishment. Group 8 was headed up by Dr Herbert Skinner, with a team of Scientific Officers who included L E Mussell and J R (Jimmy) Atkinson. Reg Batt was a member of this Group, which would take on the development of 3 cm AI for the Firefly. Group 9 would be responsible for 3 cm ASV for the Barracuda.

As a security precaution, TRE assigned 'Item Numbers' to its allocated research and development tasks. Item 45, assigned in early 1942, was 'Test of AIX in Fulmar and Firefly' even though availability of a Firefly was far away (the term AIX was used as shorthand for X-band AI radar). Aircraft allocated to this project were the Boeing, together with Fulmar II N1859, which being the precursor of the Firefly as the Navy's two seat fighter, was seen as a useful stand-in, pending the availability of a Firefly. In the event, equipping the Fulmar took a long time, so the Boeing carried the full burden of the experimental work. In any event, it was probably felt that it would be better to prove the system in the Boeing before moving to the cramped confines of the Fulmar.

By April 1942, installation of the experimental 3 cm radar in the Boeing was under way and by early May 1942, the more fundamental problems in designing the 3 cm radar had been resolved. A magnetron for the new wavelength had been developed, and all the elements of the waveguide transmit and receive system had been defined.

At 3 cm, the use of waveguides to connect the aerial most efficiently to the transmitter/receiver complex was regarded as essential. These waveguides were thin-walled metal tubes, rectangular in cross-section. Following the transfer of the Boeing from Hurn to Defford, work on modifying DZ203 continued without delay, as the changes needed for its new role evolved. Installation of the scanner for 3 cm radar[74] progressed, with scanner controls being fitted to cabin bench instrument trays, along with installation of the complex wiring required. A variety of other 'mods', in progress or complete, featured in TRE workshop reports throughout the first half of 1942. By the time the aircraft arrived at Defford at the end of May 1942, all trays, with the exception of a modulator tray, which was being supplied by TRE, had been manufactured and installed. Preparation of a connector schedule, alternator and DC wiring were in hand. Most of the waveguide system was installed but was awaiting installation of the modulator for its completion. The X-band waveguides were significantly smaller in cross-section (25 x 12.5 mm) than those which might be used for S-band (typically70 x 34 mm).[75]

During the month of March 1942, Frank Griffiths made a series of flights in the Boeing, each time accompanied by passengers. On the 8th he flew to Boscombe Down and Abingdon with four passengers; on the 9th from Hurn to Ballykelly and St Angelo in Northern Ireland, with six passengers, and on the 10th to St Angelo, Ballykelly, Ballyherbert, the Isle of Man and back to Hurn, with seven passengers. The airfields visited in this round trip have a strong Royal Navy or Coastal Command flavour, marking the new phase of the radar research career of the Boeing, which was now shifting to anti-submarine and other applications of 3 cm radar. This nautical impression is reinforced by a trip on 19th March, when Griffiths delivered a Walrus to Harrowbeer in Devon, accompanied by Lt Usher of the US Army, and returned from Harrowbeer to Hurn the same day piloting the Boeing with five passengers.

One consequence of the commitment of the Boeing to the AIX research was that TFU lost the use of this aircraft for passenger-carrying and communications purposes, in which role the Boeing, with its heated and sound-proofed cabin, had understandably proved popular and useful. At the TFU monthly progress meeting in April 1942, a replacement was sought for the Boeing for ferrying pilots and apparatus - a Lockheed Electra or similar aircraft was desired. Eventually, an Airspeed Envoy was provided.[76]

In May 1942, the organisational structure of TFU at Defford consisted of three main sections – Defensive, Offensive and Naval. The Boeing was initially allotted to 'B' Flight of the Offensive Section. Sqn Ldr Frank Griffiths was OC 'B' Flight while OC Offensive Section was Wg Cdr Horner.

On 4th June, Griffiths piloted the Boeing with seven passengers on a return flight to RAF Valley in Anglesey. During this, he flew over Hilbre Island just off the north-west tip of the Wirral peninsula in the estuary of the River Dee. A wreck of a ship aground on Hoylake Sands near Hilbre Island was envisaged a suitable target for 3 cm ASV. It appears the wreck was already being used by aircraft from Defford, for 10 cm wavelength 'blind bombing' trials, with an Anson circling at low level to record the fall of smoke bombs dropped from an 'H₂S' equipped aircraft at higher altitude. Griffiths may have been guided in the choice of this area for 3 cm ASV trials because he knew well the sands of the Dee, having sailed and fished in these waters before the war. On board the Boeing with him on 4th June, were two

pilots from 'B' Flight, Fg Off Frank Brown and Plt Off Routledge; the TRE scientist in charge of the 3 cm trials, Mr L E Mussell; and Douglas Fisher from the TRE Photographic Section.

(Left) *Fg Off Frank Brown in the passenger cabin of Boeing 247-D DZ203, noting readings on a clip board during a flight from RAF Valley in connection with X-band trials.*[77] (Douglas Fisher Collection)

The X-band team from TFU Defford, on the beach near RAF Valley, waiting for the tide to turn before checking the suitability of the wreck near Hilbre Island as a target for 3cm ASV trials. Left to right: *Plt Off Routledge, Fg Off Frank Brown, unknown, unknown, Sqn Ldr Frank Griffiths, Mr L E Mussell the TRE Scientific Officer in charge of the trials.* (Douglas Fisher Collection)

Because of the planned use of the Boeing for ASV trials over the sea, the need was identified for a quick release modification to the doors, which was completed by the end of June 1942. During that month, the Boeing is reported as *'Gone away to Wroughton'* but for what purpose it went to the base of No. 15 Maintenance Unit (MU) and for how long is not recorded, though it may have been in connection with the quick release modification to the doors.

On 10th July 1942, a notice was issued by the Ministry of Aircraft Production (MAP), ordering that for the purpose of the X-band trials, the Boeing be placed in the MAP's 'Top Secret' category. This was to be indicated by painting the 'G' symbol on the Boeing, applied after the serial as 'DZ203/G'. This served to indicate that this very valuable and secret aircraft should be under armed guard at all times when on the ground.

A grounded wreck in the Dee estuary, thought to be that of SS Nestos. The hull has broken in two, and the aft part has sunk in deeper water.[78] *The wreck is being used as target for smoke bombs in H_2S trials.* (Douglas Fisher Collection)

The Boeing 247-D of TFU was almost certainly the only civil airliner ever to be distinguished with this high security 'Top Secret' designation.[79]

Through the summer of 1942, 'Aircraft Weekly State' returns from TFU show that the dispersal point for DZ203 was on the grass, but by the start of October, more hangars had been built at Defford, and the Boeing was suitably housed in one of these.

The Boeing was now used intensively on an initial flight trials programme with 3 cm radar, which lasted from early July to mid October 1942. The 3 cm radar installation was tested in three roles - AI, ASV and H_2S (ground mapping for navigation and 'blind bombing'). The work is summarised in a report[80] by L E Mussell, a Scientific Officer in Group 8 at TRE. This describes how the equipment was tested with two sizes of what were referred to as 'mirrors' (parabolic reflectors), 16 inch and 30 inch diameter, giving beam angles of 8 degrees and 3 degrees respectively.

In the AI mode, a Whitley was used as a target and in the 'end on' position this gave a strong echo with the 16 inch reflector at 2½ - 3 miles range. Later, the 30 inch reflector was used to detect a Wellington. On one run, flying at 4,000 feet, the target was picked up at ½ mile range and followed out to 7 miles.

(Left) *Plt Off Jack Routledge, one of the Boeing pilots during the X-band trials.* (Douglas Fisher Collection)

Various targets were chosen for ASV tests. A buoy standing 17 feet out of the water (and thus not dissimilar to the conning tower of a U-boat running awash) was detected at 5 miles from an altitude of 500 feet with the 16 inch reflector.

The second target selected was the wreck of a 5,000 ton ship, whose fairly complete hull varied from being almost totally exposed at low tide, to almost covered at high tide. The wreck, described as being off Hoylake in the Dee estuary, was almost certainly that of the SS *Nestos*, a Greek steamer which ran aground on Hoyle Sands on 2nd April 1941, and was later used by the RAF as a target for bombing practice. As Hoyle Sands lie adjacent to Hoylake and Hilbre Islands, this explains the flight of Griffiths and the X-band team over this area in the Boeing on 4th June. It is assumed that the Boeing was based at Valley for the X-band trials. The wreck was detected at 10 miles range from 1,000 feet with the 16 inch reflector at low tide, and 12 miles with the 30 inch reflector at half tide.

The third target for 3 cm ASV trials was Bell Rock Lighthouse, 12 miles offshore from Arbroath in Angus, east of the Firth of Tay in Scotland. For this purpose the Boeing was on detached duty for around two weeks at the Royal Naval Air Station at Arbroath, departing from Defford on 9th September, and returning at an uncertain date later in the month. Arbroath was home to 783 Squadron, a naval unit specialising in radar instruction. Bell Rock lighthouse was detected at 3 miles range from 1,500 feet with the 16 inch reflector, and at 6 miles from 500 feet with the 30 inch reflector (although it was reported as 'not seen' from 2,000ft with the latter). Finally on the ASV trials, the radar was tested using a variety of ships at sea as targets, mostly between 1,000 and 3,000 tons, although no large ships were observed and no correlation between size and range was attempted.

Minimising 'sea clutter' (unwanted signals reflected from the surface of the sea) was regarded as a most important consideration with ASV, but none was observed when flying with the beam horizontal at 1,000 feet with the 16 inch or 1,500 feet with the 30 inch reflector. With the beam depressed, sea clutter was seen at ranges less than 4 miles with the 16 inch or 8 miles with 30 inch reflector, but in no case was it so strong that a land or ship 'return' could not be followed through it.

The third series of tests of the 3 cm radar during this period was for the 'H$_2$S' ground mapping application. Using both sizes of reflector, very good representations of coastlines, wide river estuaries and islands, including low sandy areas, were obtained. The discrimination was good enough to show a 1 mile long bridge and its approach at 14 miles range; a water channel 250 yards wide at 5 miles; and small piers at 3 to 4 miles range. Although the distinction between land and water became less marked with increasing altitude, the definition of towns and built up areas did not decrease similarly, and at 7,000 feet these areas were still clearly seen (for example, Warrington was seen from 30 miles). From 5,000 feet, the division of Chester by the River Dee could be picked out at a range of 8 miles. Photographic records were kept of flights along the Firth of Tay; over Montrose Basin (north of Arbroath); and along the Dee estuary.

The trials of 3 cm radar were not without their difficulties. The petrol engine driven APU sets in the Boeing which supplied the power for the radar were the cause of 50% of the failures recorded. There were problems with various components, including magnets, protectors, potentiometers, and valves, as well as magnetron replacements needed, and power adjustments having to be carried out, amongst many other problems. All this gives a vivid picture of the way the scientists had to struggle with delicate and fallible equipment, even in the relative space and comfort of the cabin of the Boeing.

The engineering staff on the ground were also kept busy in support of the trials, with workshop reports during August continuing to record 'mods' to the 3 cm scanner. Scientists and engineers were not helped by the shortage of laboratory and workshop facilities at Defford, where buildings were still being erected to accommodate TRE staff and TFU personnel following the move from Hurn. RAF Defford, just as Hurn had been, was an uncompleted airfield at this time, and had consisted of little more than a completed triangular pattern of runways when TFU had moved in just a few months previously.

The dust jacket of Reg Batt's book 'The Radar Army' reproduces a splendid photograph supplied to him by J R (Jimmy) Atkinson, said to be an inveterate pipe smoker, who is shown standing on a ladder, pipe in mouth, supervising work in the open, on the experimental 3 cm radar in the nose compartment of the Boeing, assisted by Lt Bob Doran of the USAAF and a Fleet Air Arm radar mechanic. The aircraft appears to be close to an oak tree, typical of those in Croome Park which provided useful cover from aerial observation around the Defford airfield technical site. As will be related, much later one of these ancient trees may have played a part in the demise of DZ203.

By early October 1942, when Mussell reported on the comprehensive trials in the Boeing of 3 cm radar for AI, ASV and H₂S applications, Fulmar N1859 was still at its manufacturers, Fairey Aviation, where it had been for nearly six months for fitting of the scanner and other equipment supplied by TRE. The delay, it was said, was caused by modifications to the scanner. In monthly reports from TFU, the title of project 'Item 45' had been simplified to 'Tests of AIX', involving only the Boeing, which flew 25 hours on X-band AI trials in the month of September. A separate project on 3 cm radar for ASV had been set up, entitled 'Item 62: Tests of ASVX', aimed at the Barracuda requirement. The second prototype Barracuda P1770, had been modified to become the prototype of the Mk II radar equipped version, and was first flown in this form on 17th August.[81] It was now at RNAS Arbroath marked P1770/G, and may have been there at the same time in September as the Boeing when the latter was carrying

A rare photo showing DZ203 during the phase of its career while it was being used for trials on 3 cm wavelength radar, from the dust-cover of The Radar Army *by Reg Batt, 1991, where it was captioned*: 'J.R. Atkinson, a research scientist, supervising work on an experimental 3 cm radar on the Boeing, assisted by Lt. Bob Doran, USAAF and a Fleet Air Arm radar mechanic, photo courtesy of J.R. Atkinson'. *The 'radome' nose has been removed to reveal the scanner. The photo neatly captures the Allied cross-services spirit of radar research at TFU Defford, combining as it does a civilian scientist, pipe in mouth, an American technical officer, and a Royal Navy radar mechanic.* (Reproduction of photo by kind permission of Robert Hale Limited)

out its ASV trials from this very busy airfield.[82] While availability of the Barracuda was awaited at Defford, Hudson AM907/G was allocated to the project, and fitted out with ASVX equipment during October 1942. Meanwhile, the Boeing soldiered on, flying a further 10½ hours on X-band trials in the month of November.

The replacement for the Boeing 247-D in the popular role it fulfilled for a few months before the start of X-band project, as a general light transport and communications aircraft, arrived in the form of Airspeed Envoy III DG663. The Envoy, formerly G-ADAZ, 'Tynedale' of North Eastern Airlines, was not as comfortable or as commodious as either the Boeing or the Lockheed 10 Electra requested, but it was soon kept busy. Griffiths used the Envoy for a round trip to Boscombe Down on July 17th 1942, with four passengers to Chivenor on July 23rd, and on six or seven more flights while the Boeing was away at Valley and Arbroath. Later Griffiths used the Envoy to return from Yate after delivering Parnell Hendy Heck G-AEGH. The Envoy was even used for 'experimental' work, presumably as a target.

During August 1942, it is recorded[83] that the Boeing carried out experiments with Mark III IFF installed. 'Identification Friend or Foe'

Airspeed Envoy III DG663 at Defford. (Douglas Fisher Collection)

(IFF) was a vital 'secondary' radar system (AI, ASV, and H_2S being examples of primary radars) intended automatically to prevent misidentification of friendly aircraft as enemy aircraft. In its simplest wartime form, an Allied radar (ground or airborne) transmitted a specially coded 'interrogating' pulse together with its primary pulse transmission. All Allied front line aircraft were fitted with a small receiver/transmitter (an IFF 'transponder') which received the interrogating signal and automatically responded with a pre-determined, coded, recognition signal. Reception of the correct transponder response by the interrogating radar resulted in automatic marking of friendly targets on an interceptor's radar display. 'Identification Friend or Foe' is somewhat of a misnomer, as IFF can only positively identify friendly targets, not hostile ones. If an IFF interrogation receives no reply or an invalid one, the object cannot be identified as friendly, but is not positively identified as a foe.

The use of transponders also led to the development of homing devices, in the form of transponder 'beacons' which responded to a signal from an aircraft. There were to be many other applications of this concept. First of all though, the advent of radar operating at 3 cm, demanded the development of IFF triggered by this wavelength.

Regarding the work on 3 cm radar, Sir Bernard Lovell noted in his autobiography, that in the early autumn of 1942, a group at TRE, which included J R Atkinson, was working in close collaboration with the Admiralty Valve Laboratory at the University of Birmingham. This group, he wrote, was responsible for a 3 cm radar being fitted in the Boeing, for blind bombing trials, which resulted in production arrangements to meet a Fleet Air Arm requirement. However, successful trials at low altitude in the 'H_2S' mode were regarded as 'misleading' by Bomber Command whose requirement was for operations at 20,000 feet. As an interesting footnote, Lovell wrote: *'I am informed by J R Atkinson, who was in charge of the 3 cm installation in this aeroplane, that it was not the Boeing originally fitted with American centimetre AI equipment. He believes it was an executive passenger aeroplane already in this country'.*[84] All the evidence suggests that either Lovell or Atkinson was misinformed, for

DZ203 was the only Boeing 247-D operating in this country during the Second World War, or indeed at any other time.

One of the pilots who flew the Boeing during this period was Ronald Bain Thompson, who served at Defford from February to September 1942, when he was posted to Coastal Command to command 206 Squadron at Lagens on the Azores, which had just become available to Britain as a base to counter the mid-Atlantic U-boat threat. He retired from the RAF in 1963 with the rank of Air Vice-Marshal.

When the TFU moved to Defford in April 1942, the airfield had runways but few buildings and no hangars. An intensive programme of building works commenced to meet the needs of radar research. Workshops, laboratories, offices, stores and accommodation areas, were erected across the eastern part of Croome Park. Meanwhile, the Boeing had to stand outside on a grass dispersal area, and be maintained in the open until the first hangars were erected. This view across the main technical site at the northern end of the airfield, shows the first hangar to be erected, Hangar No. 1. An Anson stands outside the hangar, and behind it in the hangar, can be glimpsed the Boeing 247-D DZ203. (RAF Defford Reunion Association via Dennis Williams).

Frank Griffiths did not pilot the Boeing on the 3 cm trials, apart perhaps one flight on 13th October, with four passengers, recorded in his log book as 'experimental'. But he still had some contact with DZ203/G. On 17th July, he flew with Ronald Bain Thompson to Boscombe Down in Envoy DG663, shortly before giving Thompson his first experience of piloting the Boeing on 1st August. On 19th September, after the return of the Boeing from Arbroath, Griffiths provided 'FP' (flying practice?) for Lt Stanley Adams RN. Adams, who became a close friend of Griffiths, was appointed to command the Naval Section of TFU while the unit was at Hurn, and continued in this post for the first six months at Defford. On 26th October, Griffith flew 1 hour dual with Sgt Lewis, adding yet another name to the list of pilots authorised to fly the Boeing.

At Defford, 3rd October 1942 was something of a red letter day as Sir Archibald Sinclair, Secretary of State for Air, came for a demonstration which included the 3 cm radar in the Boeing.

In November 1942, having helped to develop an IFF system to work with 3 cm radar, DZ203/G was now required for trials of a homing system using a transponder beacon. A transponder beacon located at an airfield, and used by radar-fitted aircraft for homing to that airfield, was not a new concept, having been introduced as an operating mode of early 1.5 metre wavelength systems. Dr Hanbury Brown, the TRE scientist involved, relates how the introduction of a transponder beacon at base, enabled aircrews to find their way home safely in all weather conditions - thus helping to convince ASV radar operators of the value of the early recalcitrant sets with which they were struggling![85] Unsurprisingly, beacons were equally appreciated by night-fighter pilots returning to base. This universal appreciation ensured that Beacon Mode became a feature of 10 cm radar systems. Now that the Boeing was flying on 3 cm system trials, X-band beacon development became part of its tasking. Because the Fleet Air Arm had become the prime mover in 3 cm system development, a new feature of X-band beacon was that it could also be sited on an aircraft carrier. Accordingly, the Boeing and the Naval Section became associated with TFU Item 111 'ASVX Beaconry'. Installations to equip the Boeing for this role were in hand at the start of December 1942 and complete, or partly so, by the end of the month.

Reports from the workshops at Defford show that during November 1942, the Boeing had been fitted with a 'transmitting aerial for beaconry, dipole and director' mounted under the port wing, near the tip. Part at least of this installation was reported to be a Fulmar AI '4 El' aerial[86] modified to suit a frequency of 235 MHz. There was further work in December on the El aerial on the port wing of the Boeing, and on its scanner and radome nose, while other equipment was being overhauled. Work on the transmitting aerial for the 'beaconry' project took some time while Defford awaited drawings which were being prepared by TRE during December.

This work dragged on into January 1943, and was still only 85% complete by the middle of that month. Other tasks at this time involved modifications to the petrol-engine powered APUs for higher altitude work. The work on the transmitting aerials was not complete until towards the end of January – the slow progress suggests other priorities may have taken over at Malvern and Defford.

Mr J Banner, a TRE Experimental Officer based at Defford, was in charge of this project, working closely with Lt Cdr A E Milward, who had taken over as Commanding Officer of the Naval Section. At the TFU monthly progress meeting on 29th January 1943, Banner said he had been asked to co-operate with the RN Signal School on the Isle of Man for 'AIX' tests. It was agreed the Boeing could land on the island at Andreas airfield but it was noted that the Navy might have difficulty maintaining it and providing the 24 hour guard required by its '/G' status. Therefore, it was suggested it would be better to operate on a daily basis from Valley, landing as necessary on the Isle of Man.

Meanwhile, more pilots joined the programme being flown by the Boeing. On 29th December, Fg Off Geoffrey Wirdnam was introduced to the aircraft when he flew on an experimental flight lasting 2 hours 10 minutes, as second pilot to Flt Lt Mountford, who appears to have been one of the regular pilots of the Boeing around this time.

HMS Saltburn, *a coal burning minesweeper of the 'Improved Hunt' class, used in conjunction with the Boeing for X-band ASV trials in the Irish Sea. HMS* Saltburn *was launched in 1918. The ship spent most of the Second World War as a tender to the Navigation School HMS* Dryad *for training at Portsmouth, but was evidently released from these duties for use in the radar trials.* (Courtesy Naval History Flixweb-site)

Defford workshop reports show further 'beacon TX aerial mods'[87] in January and February 1943. The flights to the Isle of Man went ahead, with the Boeing arriving at Andreas on 9th February, for trials over the Irish Sea involving HMS *Saltburn* [88], which was an improved Hunt class coal-fired minesweeper dating from the First World War. On the 22nd of the month the Boeing was due to fly back from Andreas, as trials continued, but was forced to land out at Hawarden owing to adverse weather. The TRE monthly progress meeting on 26th February was told that the Boeing was needed for further trials at Defford when it returned from the Isle of Man.

On 17th March, Wirdnam flew again in the Boeing at Defford, dual with Griffiths on an 'E&A' (Engines and Airframe) test, and then radio training for Wren Gallup (Griffiths refers to the WRNS personnel who flew with him as *'unsung heroines of cold, sick-making trips – yet what a contribution they made to winning the battle of the Atlantic!'*).[89]

The X-band trials were being carried out primarily on behalf of the Fleet Air Arm, so on 27th March, Frank Griffiths took the opportunity to convert Lt Cdr Milward to type on the Boeing, and to introduce him to the application of its airborne 3 cm radar.

The following day, 28th March 1943, Griffiths piloted DZ203/G on a flight to Macrihanish accompanied by Professor Oliphant, Dr Skinner of TRE, and six crew. Macrihanish, three miles west of Campbeltown on the Mull of Kintyre, was a Naval air station, home to 772 Fleet Requirements Unit, with an assortment of aircraft. Professor Oliphant was head of the group working on magnetron research at the University of Birmingham – his laboratory, previously known as the Mond Laboratory, became the Admiralty Research Laboratory at Birmingham in 1939. Sir Mark Oliphant (as he later became) had been recruited by Tizard to work on the atomic bomb, but on this occasion, in the company of Dr Herbert Skinner of TRE, we may assume his interest was in aspects of 3 cm radar.

By the start of April 1943 the tests on the Isle of Man had been completed, and the Boeing was back at Defford having new APU sets installed. The future programme involved further tests with the Admiralty Signals Establishment (ASE) on the Isle of Man.

The monthly return on projects and aircraft allocated, dated 30th April, suggested more work on the 'X-beaconry' project (Item 111) for which the Boeing was the only aircraft allocated. ASE had produced a mobile beacon which was being subjected to tests on the ground at Defford, and flight trials were to begin when these had produced satisfactory results. At the monthly meeting, Dr Lewis confirmed that ground beacons

(Left) *Flt Lt R.H. Mountford, who flew the Boeing regularly on X-band trials. He was killed in action in March 1944.* (Douglas Fisher Collection)

were being developed by ASE, with TFU aircraft being required for trials.

However, Mr Banner now told the meeting that it was felt the Boeing was unsuitable for this work, and a programme had been arranged to test the ASE beacon on the Isle of Man using a Swordfish fitted with ASVX.

Despite the rejection of the Boeing for this part of the 'X-beaconry' project, it remained active on behalf of the Naval Section at Defford. A surviving fragment of a DI (Daily Inspections) log entry dated 16th May 1943, shows that the Naval Section was required to sign for work on DZ203/G.

At the progress meeting on 28th May, Mr Atkinson introduced a new project, Item 130. He explained that the Navy had asked for an ASVX system suitable for single-seat fighters. This was confirmed by Cdr Grenfell, and it was agreed the work should commence using the Boeing. However, Sqn Ldr Gilliard of TFU pointed out that the Boeing was beginning to show signs of its age. After some discussion, it was agreed to carry out the 'bread-board' stage in an Anson that was to be taken on charge, while work to modify the Boeing went ahead. A report covering the period 25th June to 22nd July, stated that installation in the Boeing of equipment for the single-seat ASVX project was almost complete, and air tests were about to begin, although the Anson had still not arrived.

Monthly progress meetings at Defford were routinely chaired by the Station Commander, and at the meeting on 30th July 1943, with Gp Capt King in the chair, Mr Atkinson asked about a replacement for the Boeing for basic experimental work. From this it may be concluded that the decision had been taken not to proceed with the Boeing after the single-seat ASVX trials, because of its condition. Atkinson was told a replacement would be found, type to be decided later.

Meanwhile, the Boeing 247-D flying around in British skies had not passed unnoticed. A reader's letter to the 'Aeroplane Spotter', published in the edition of 23rd September 1943, reported *'On two occasions recently a Boeing 247-D has been seen flying over'*. The Editor responded by saying only one 247-D was flying in this country, and printed a photo of the 'MacRobertson' Race 247-D retouched by adding British markings in the form then current, having narrow yellow and white rings in the roundels, with the intention of showing what this 247-D might look like.

At the end of August 1943, the Boeing spent several days at Chivenor in Devon after flying there from Defford on the 25th of the month. Chivenor was an important Coastal Command airfield, so the Boeing may have been there on an ASVX trials detachment (a buoy in Barnstaple bay was used as a target by aircraft on 3 cm trials flying from Chivenor). But equally it could simply have been the means of travel for a group of TRE scientists. The Chivenor ORB says on 26th August: *'Mr Stewart visited to film ASV installations in a Halifax, and Halifax aircraft in flight'.*[90] John Stewart was a major figure in the Photography and Film Department at Malvern, and was responsible for 35 mm filming. He was a friend and colleague of Douglas Fisher, who carried out 16 mm filming, and who later built up and digitised the extensive collection of wartime photographs which carries his name. An entry in the Defford Controller's Watch Log dated 26th August, records of the Boeing: *'At Chivenor return postponed'*, and on the 28th, the Boeing was still at Chivenor. The Chivenor ORB records that on 28th August: *'Mr Rennie of TRE visited to instruct radar personnel in modifications to monitor type for operation with R.3190'.* The ORB further states that there was no flying at Chivenor on the 28th, and no operations on the 29th owing to the weather. Nevertheless, on the 29th the Boeing departed Chivenor to return to Defford. Mr C A Rennie was a member of Group 25 (Post Design Services), a large and active Group at TRE, concerned with implementation in service of new radar equipment.[91]

On 19th September 1943, it was decided that the Boeing had no further usefulness for radar research. It suffered the indignity of being stripped of its MAP Top Secret '/G' status on 20th September. The record states it was to be transferred to the TFU Communications flight, to serve as a general light transport and communications hack.

In this role, it was intended to replace an Envoy, L7270, which was formerly G-AEXX of the King's Flight.[92]

All this is recorded on the Boeing's history card, MAP Form 2101, and appeared to confirm unambiguously that the end of the road had been reached as far as its use in radar research was concerned. What the scientists of TRE, who held the Boeing in such high regard, thought about this decision is not recorded, so one can only speculate.

Be that as it may, it appears that at some point in September 1943, presumably after the date of the entry in the Form 2101, the Boeing was reprieved.

Frank Griffiths started the Second World War as a lowly Pilot Officer, but by the end of the war achieved the rank of Group Captain at BLEU, by which time he was established as an influential figure in the field of airborne radar. During his time at TFU, it was his lot to attend innumerable meetings involving scientists, senior officers, civil servants and other services. With his impatience to solve problems and win the war, his frustration sometimes manifested itself, as in this photo probably taken by his friend Douglas Fisher. The placard reads: 'A Conference is a gathering of Important People who, singly, can do nothing, but together, can decide that nothing can be done'. (Douglas Fisher Collection).

Gp Capt John McDonald assumed command at Defford on 2nd October 1943, and with the hand-over under way, was present at the TFU monthly progress meeting[93] held on the previous day, 1st October, with Gp Capt King still in the chair. At this meeting, Gp Capt McDonald, as Station Commander designate, stated that the Boeing would not be available after its next inspection. He said it had been arranged for it to be used for communications flying, but this would now not be possible and an alternative twin-engine aircraft suitable for eight passengers was required. In the Table covering aircraft utilisation in the period 26th August to 22nd September 1943, the Boeing was recorded as having flown 16 hours in these four weeks, with air tests in progress. It was noted that, for ASVX trials, the Boeing was expected to be replaced by a Hudson, and when the latter arrived, equipment would be transferred to it from the Boeing.

At the end of October 1943, the Boeing was still listed under Item 130 (X-band development for the Fleet Air Arm, as part of the Offensive Section of TFU), with new equipment being installed and flight tests continuing. However, Hudson T9339 had arrived, and equipment was being installed in this aircraft. This state of affairs continued into November, when the Hudson was recorded as flying on ASVX development trials. For the period ending 30th December 1943, there was a similar entry for the Boeing, which had flown just two hours over five weeks, but there was no further mention of the Hudson under the project heading of X-band. Finally, at the end of January1944, Gp Capt McDonald was minuted as stating that the Boeing had very few useful hours left, and that even if, after the review of the X-band programme, a 'flying laboratory' were still required, the Boeing would be unavailable.

It was agreed at the monthly meeting on 2nd February 1944, that the Boeing should be released and the item deleted. During this final month of the Boeing's last work on X-band development for the Fleet Air Arm, it flew a further two hours testing a high-speed scanner.

With the benefit of hindsight, its seems likely that McDonald was unwilling to allow the Boeing to go to the Communications Flight and countermanded a decision taken under his predecessor in September 1943. McDonald had other plans for the old airliner, but for the time being wished to keep it available. It is not known whether the decision to remove the '/G' symbol (recorded on 20th September) had been reversed, but this seems unlikely. Perhaps by this time it was felt that the threat of German spies on the ground (if that threat had ever existed), had receded.

Going back to the flight by Frank Griffiths to the Mull of Kintyre on 28th March 1943, this was to be his last in the Boeing for some time. On 21st April, he was posted to 138 Squadron at Tempsford, to fly supply operations to the French Resistance. After completing numerous operations, on the night of 14th/15th August his Halifax crashed near Annecy, close to the Swiss border, and he was the sole

Firefly NF Mk II fitted with 3 cm AI radar and scanner mounted in a pod on the wing. (Crown copyright)

survivor. He evaded capture, and after remarkable adventures[94], returned to England, flying from Gibraltar as a passenger in a Warwick, which was struck by lightning en route, arriving at Lyneham on 30th November. After a short period of rest and recuperation, he returned to Defford as Officer Commanding Flying in January 1944.

In view of the high regard, indeed affection, Griffiths held for the old Boeing, it is perhaps not entirely fanciful to suppose its fortunes went into a decline on his departure, only to come back into favour on his return. By the time of Griffiths' return, the role of the Boeing in the development of 3 cm radar had virtually finished. The work on 3 cm

AIX for the Firefly NFII was shelved. It had become a victim of its own complexity, being too large and heavy, and there were inherent problems with the 'lock-follow' system.[95] Interest in 3 cm AI was revived urgently in mid 1944 to meet the threat of fast low flying V1 weapons. As it happened though, the Allies overran the enemy launching sites before 3 cm AI could be brought into use for the interception of V1s.

Versions of H_2S (Marks III and IV) operating in the 3 cm band were developed, initially intended for use by the Pathfinders of Bomber Command, but also in anticipation of more effective German countermeasures against 10 cm wavelength radar. The 3 cm H_2S was given priority over the 3 cm ASV intended for Coastal Command, although 3 cm radar for the Barracuda ultimately emerged as ASV Mark XI.[96] However, work on 3 cm ASV for Coastal Command suddenly became urgent in October 1944 with the advent of a new class of U-boat fitted with a 'Schnorkel' breathing tube, which enabled a submarine to recharge its batteries while remaining submerged. Schnorkel tubes were virtually undetectable by 10 cm radar, so the greater resolution of 3 cm was needed for aircraft to spot them. Accordingly, as a very rapid development that drew on the outcome of the X-band trials, ASV Mk VII was produced as a comparatively simple conversion of ASV Mk III 10 cm radar. Tests on more refined forms of 3 cm ASV in this role were not concluded before the end of the war[97], although X-band radar went on to play a vital part in Cold War ASV developments.

The requirement for AI radar in naval night fighters would be met by an American radar, 3 cm AN/APS-4, for the Firefly NFI. This was tested operationally from RAF Coltishall in October and November 1944 against He111 aircraft which were carrying and launching V1 'flying bombs' over the North Sea. Later marks of Firefly were fitted with AN/APS-6 radar (this 3 cm AI system doubling as ASV).

The single-seat fighter requirement was met very successfully by AN/APS-6 in the night-fighter F6F-3N Hellcat of the US Navy, which was also used in small numbers by the Fleet Air Arm as the Hellcat NFII, in the late stages of the war in the Pacific in which the Royal Navy was active.[98]

Fairey Barracuda III DP855/G, fitted with ASVX radar, believed to be ASV Mk XI, an outcome of the X-band trials with 'The Boeing'. Barracuda DP855/G was based at Defford, and used for ASVX trials through the first half of 1944. (Crown Copyright via Sqn Ldr Mike Dean)

For the RAF, 3 cm AI in the form of AI Mk XV using American AN/APS-4 components, was installed in Mosquito night fighters, and used successfully near the end of the war.[99]

Meanwhile, 3 cm H_2S for bombing by the RAF had been giving mixed results, although the Americans pressed on with their 3 cm version, referred to as H_2X, which had actually been first demonstrated in the United States in 1943, in another Boeing 247-D.[100]

The pioneering work on X-band radar in the Boeing successfully demonstrated the technology needed for the production of X-band H_2S and ASV, both of which were well into service prior to the end of the Second World War, and led to initial combat trials with X-band AI radar in night fighters. Although development of AIX for the Firefly NFII had been abandoned, the effort had not been wasted as it resulted in a set of basic 3 cm units which provided the core components for other systems. 'Lock-follow', also developed for AIX, became a key part of Cold War AI and guided missile technology. The development of X-band radar, which had been initiated with the Boeing, was to continue in Britain, the United States and elsewhere, and has dominated airborne radar, right up to the present time.

Group Captain John McDonald CBE, AFC, Station Commander at RAF Defford, who was a driving force behind the successful automatic landing trials with Boeing 247-D DZ203, from 1944. (Michael McDonald)

8. AUTOMATIC BLIND LANDING

When Frank Griffiths returned to Defford towards the end of January 1944, after his adventures in France and Spain, and having been away for nine months, inevitably he found much had changed. There were now over two thousand military and civilian personnel based at Defford, and the variety of radar projects was greater than ever. RAF and Royal Navy personnel of TFU continued to maintain and fly the aircraft, while civilian TRE staff designed, manufactured, installed and modified radar and other electronic systems.

Griffiths found he was reporting to the new Station Commander, Group Captain John A McDonald, who had taken up the appointment at Defford at the start of October 1943, on his return from a staff job in India.

Gp Capt McDonald, familiarly known as 'Mac' by everyone in the RAF from Air Chief Marshal Sir John Slessor[101] downwards, was born in 1898, and had a long career in the RAF starting in the First World War. In January 1921, he joined HQ Communications Flight at Northolt as a young Pilot Officer with 56 hours flying time in his log book. The Chanak Crisis in Turkey in 1922 forced the British Government to rush reinforcements to the area, and 'Mac' was posted to No.4 Squadron. He and his fellow pilots flew their Bristol Fighters off the deck of HMS *Argus* to land in the Dardanelles neutral zone, even though none of them had flown off an aircraft carrier before. Later, this experience was put to good use when forces were rushed to the crisis in Shanghai in 1927, and 'Mac' had to learn quickly to fly floatplanes as well as landplanes. After serving with various operational squadrons in the UK, he was posted to India in 1943, only to return to England in the autumn to assume command at Defford.

On arrival at Defford, 'Mac' found morale had been dented by a number of fatal crashes. Experimental test flying of radar could be a dangerous business for aircrew and scientists alike.[102] He set about restoring morale by leading from the front. He had had only limited opportunity to fly in India, mostly piloting a communications Vega Gull, so now he set about getting as much flying as he could, initially on Hurricanes and Spitfires, then graduating to larger multi-engine types, of which there was no lack of choice at Defford.

A new project, Automatic Landing, was emerging and McDonald, drawing on his long and extraordinarily varied experience as a pilot, gave this his personal attention. At a fairly early stage, McDonald identified the Boeing 247-D as the ideal demonstrator for the system which he could see developing.

The requirement was as follows. As the war progressed, and the allied bomber fleets grew yet larger, concern had become ever greater about the problem of landing aircraft in poor visibility. Some blind landing systems existed, but these all depended on reasonable visibility near the point of touchdown, and carefully managed separation between individual landings with no great time pressure. Resolving this problem had now become a major project for TRE and TFU.

In his memoirs, Frank Griffiths later wrote:

'On return to England, it was back to the boffins at the Telecommunications Flying Unit at Defford, there to take part in one of the longed-for developments in aviation: the Automatic Landing of Aircraft'.

Griffiths was aware of the systems which were available and to some extent in use, but all had their limitations.

Until the autumn of 1943, the only available method for the RAF was Standard Blind Approach (SBA, also known as the Standard Beam Approach), a continuous-wave system which provided rapid audible dots or dashes through the pilot's earphones, indicating when the aircraft was to the left or right of the runway centreline, and sounding a steady note when it was correctly lined up. This was based on the pre-war German Lorenz system. But SBA had severe disadvantages. It depended on very accurate flying and great concentration by a skilled pilot. The signals in the pilot's earphones meant that he could not at the same time hear instructions from ground control, and there was no indication of glide path (i.e. angle of descent). Above all, the landing rate with SBA was far too slow to handle a stream of bombers returning from operations, with all seeking to land. There was also a concern that because SBA was based on the Lorenz system, German intruder night fighters would be able to use it to locate vulnerable airfields where aircraft were landing.

An alternative aid, Ground Controlled Approach (GCA) was coming into use. This was a radar based 'talk down' method, with the position of the aircraft being monitored on a screen by a controller who passed heading and rate of descent instructions to the pilot. But, as Frank Griffiths observed, GCA '... *could not cope with large numbers of tired, recently-frightened pilots often in damaged aircraft and short of fuel all trying to get priority for a landing'*.

Griffiths continued:

'A fresh urgency was given to the blind landing problem when the American Air Force arrived. They thought that the English climate was atrocious... They had little use for the blind landing aids so far invented'.

'Early in 1944 a team came from the United States to demonstrate a new system of assisted landings known then as Signals Corps System 51, subsequently abbreviated to ILS (Instrument Landing System). The team was headed by a Lieutenant Colonel Francis L Moseley, formerly a development engineer for the Sperry Company and largely responsible for ILS, and his assistant Frank B Brady, who had worked with Moseley for some time. ILS was good and it did work, and it could handle aircraft far quicker than any previous system. It was fairly simple and easy to use from the pilot's point of view. Just two needles, one hanging vertically which told the pilot to turn left or right to line up with the runway, and another normally horizontal which moved up and down and gave the pilot his angle of glide'.

Instrument Landing System (ILS) is still in widespread use today as an approach aid, particularly by civil aircraft operators. Unlike GCA, ILS is a pilot-interpreted aid, based on receivers in the aircraft detecting VHF signals from two main aerodrome transmitters, known as the Glide Path and Localiser. Each of these transmitters radiates a pair of beams with modulated patterns, whose overlap defines an angle of elevation (typically 3°) for the glide path, and the extended runway centreline in azimuth for the localiser.

The development of an ILS for military use, leading to Moseley's visit and demonstrations, was the outcome of a high-level request for production of a landing aid to cope with the British weather that had so appalled Americans when the USAAF first came to Britain. But ILS was seen not as the complete answer, only part of the solution. It was an approach aid, not a fully automatic system and depended on the skill and training of the pilot, and reasonable visibility at the point of touchdown.

Moseley and Brady, having flown to England in a C-54, arrived at Defford in January 1944, together with a complete SCS-51 system, which was the military production version of the ILS developed under CAA guidance pre-war. The SCS-51 equipment had been crated and shipped from Brooklyn docks. Many years later, in 1992, Brady wrote: *'....we received a warm welcome and were introduced to the RAF officer who had been named to head up the tests. He was Frank Griffiths, a fearless Welshman who was a career officer ... Griff had very close cropped hair, a carry-over from his most recent activity. He had been shot down in the Rhone Valley while on a covert operation. A sole survivor of his four-engine bomber crew, he managed to get in the hands of the Maquis who took him to Switzerland where he spent three months recuperating from his crash injuries. He was then escorted across the occupied Rhône Valley to the Pyrénées. After walking across the mountains, he was arrested and imprisoned in Spain. The British consulate got him released and back to England, and after a week's leave, he was assigned to duty with our project with his prison haircut still in evidence'.*[103]

The ground equipment for SCS-51 was set up at Defford, and an Airspeed Oxford was fitted with the airborne part of the landing system, to be tested by Griffiths. A feature of the aircraft units was the small, circular, pilot's display. In technical terms, the unit contained two centre-zero electrical meter movements arranged so that their needles were positioned at 90 degrees to each other, with one hanging vertically. Movement of this needle away from the vertical indicated to the pilot that he was left or right of the runway and, in a complementary fashion, movement of the horizontal needle showed the pilot his deviation above or below the glidepath. SCS-51 was subsequently fitted to some 'war weary' B-24 and B-17 aircraft and tested at Defford by two USAAF pilots, Capt Stauffacher and Lt Connor, who had been assigned to the project after completing their combat tours.

Brady recalled: *'It was at this point Moseley produced a surprise ...* (he) *suggested connecting the ILS directly to the autopilot, to give a truly automatic approach. He produced a unit he had built in his own garage in Dayton, unauthorised and untested, and brought to England in his personal luggage, to provide the necessary linking system'.* The unit took the form of what Brady described as a 'bread-board' of circuitry, with two wires leading from it to the autopilot and two to the SCS-51. Moseley was allowed to test it out on a B-24 (Liberator) at Defford. The trials of this system (in February 1944) were an outstanding success.

While ILS was a radio-technology based system, TRE was working at the same time on a radar-based system, with a Mark II version of the Beam Approach Beacon System (BABS). This included a transponder which provided range as well as directional information, and became known as 'Radar BA'. The system was a development of the Rebecca-Eureka system of airborne interrogator (Rebecca) and ground-based transponder beacon (Eureka).

When approaching the airfield for landing, the Rebecca II unit in the aircraft transmitted a pulse in the 200 MHz band, which triggered a reply from the BABS II ground beacon. This had been developed from the Eureka II beacon, incorporating a double cavity switched slot antenna, to provide two overlapping beams in azimuth. The beams were switched at 8.33Hz, with transmitted pulse widths of 5µs and 12µs to port and starboard, respectively. In the aircraft, the system display used a CRT with a vertical linear time-base, with the port/starboard pulses shown respectively to left and right of it, with the ratio of their amplitudes giving a measure of the deviation from the extended runway centreline – when the pulses were equal, the aircraft was on the correct course. The position of the pulses on the vertical time-base indicated the distance to the beacon. This system was to be evaluated against the SCS-51 localiser as part of the automatic landing project. Eventually, the two systems became complimentary to each other.

In early 1944, Gp Capt McDonald wrote a series of reports on trials of various approach and homing systems. It was envisaged some of these would be brought together in a total concept, combining American SCS-51 with the British radar-based BABS beacon transponder system, to control both approach and landing. McDonald's reports included a frank, collective appraisal of the information provided by all the pilots who had undertaken the trials, since he felt their views were of paramount importance. Nevertheless, this method of assessment drew some criticism from the scientists at RAE Farnborough who were copied with the reports[104], since they evidently felt their views, not the pilots', were the more important.

Griffiths, now promoted to Wing Commander, threw himself into these trials. On only his second flight at Defford after returning from Spain, on 28th January 1944 he flew the SCS-51 equipped Oxford V4204 on what he described in his flying log as 'Experimental BA' (Beam Approach), accompanied by Flt Lt Stewart. Griffiths was soon flying 'Radar BA' in another Oxford (X7297) and trying GCA in a Stirling at St Eval. Before the end of February, Oxford V4204 fitted with SCS-51 was flown on a number of occasions by Griffiths, usually accompanied by Lt Connor of the USAAF. It appears that by March, a Wellington and a Lancaster had been fitted with SCS-51 instrumentation, and Griffiths flew both of these in the company of Moseley and Flt Lt Stewart, which may have served to convince them that these RAF bombers with their high rates of descent and marked 'flare out' before touchdown, were not suitable for the early stages of the automatic landing project.

Griffiths describes how he detailed Stewart to carry out an early trial, accompanied by Moseley operating the coupling of SCS-51 to the autopilot on a Liberator. When he returned to the Flight Office, *'Tom Stewart looked as though he'd seen a ghost. "What happened?" I asked, "Did Moseley nearly kill you?" "Good Lord, no. The darn thing worked first time and second and third! Moseley just sat beside*

Ground equipment for BABS Mk. II, showing the unique aerial system, based on a Eureka-type beacon mounted on a truck for mobility. BABS became an inherent part of the Automatic Landing system with the Boeing in 1945.

Above: *The aerial here seen folded.*

Below: *BABS Mk. II aerial unfolded and set up for use.* (Crown copyright, via Sqn Ldr Mike Dean)

me with the bread-board on his lap and an unlit cigar between his fingers. As we approached the centre line of the beam somewhere near Tewkesbury, I put in the autopilot and we came slap down the beam onto the centre of the runway. It's uncanny! It makes a better approach than I can do myself, and we did it three times…'

Through February and March 1944, a programme of automatic approach demonstrations to senior USAAF and RAF officers was carried out, on Oxford, Fortress, Lancaster, Wellington and Liberator aircraft. At the end of March, Moseley returned to Wright Field in the United States to continue work there, and Brady, Stauffacher, Connor and their technicians moved to the USAAF airbase at Bovingdon, with their trials aircraft, a B-24 which they called 'Blind Bat'. The priority was to install SCS-51 to provide ILS at key US bases. The development of coupling to other systems to give automatic landing was, as far as the Americans were concerned, seen as a longer term project for the post-war period, to be pursued at the All Weather Flying Division at Wilmington, Ohio, and at Wright Field. Fifteen SCS-51 ground facilities were installed at airfields for use by the US 8th Air Force, mostly in East Anglia, but also at Prestwick in Scotland, and at Langford Lodge in Northern Ireland.

Back at Defford, the Station Commander, Gp Capt McDonald, had been closely involved from the outset in the automatic landing project, and personally co-ordinated the project and demonstrations of its results.[105] The Boeing was the aircraft chosen for the first trials of an integrated automatic landing system, which linked SCS-51 and Radar BA to the autopilot. The Boeing had no flaps, so used a shallow approach angle and could be flown straight onto the runway to land without 'flare out'. This capability, combined with excellent stability and a low stalling speed, made the aircraft particularly suitable for the task.

It could well be that McDonald was encouraged in the decision to restore and use the Boeing by Frank Griffiths, and according to Frank Brady, the TRE staff were convinced by Moseley that at Defford they already had the very aircraft that would be ideal for automatic landing trials.

A Boeing 247-D in America impressed into military service as a C-73. Most C-73s were modified by fitting Wasp R-1340-AN-1 engines and twin bladed VP propellers similar to those fitted to DZ203 when it was refurbished at Defford in 1944. (The Boeing Company)

Moseley was well aware that Boeing 247-D aircraft, including NC13365, the 'Flying Laboratory' of United Air Lines, had proved very suitable for trials on instrument landing systems in the United States. It is reported that as an outcome of trials from as early as 1929, which came under the authority of the CAA, the first landing of a scheduled US passenger airliner assisted by a form of ILS to guide the pilot, was on 26th January 1938, when a PCA Boeing 247-D flew from Washington DC to Pittsburgh, and landed in a snowstorm.[106]

However, at Defford in early 1944, DZ203 was in poor condition and in need of not just an overhaul, but an extensive rebuild, if it were to take on the important responsibility of automatic landing development. Defford's Boeing was the only one of its kind in Britain, and must have long presented considerable problems for maintenance when it came to obtaining spare parts. It is not known to what extent support and information was received from Boeing during the war years, although a Maintenance Manual was obtained from United Air Lines. The manual supplied to Defford, which survives having been eventually deposited in the TRE Library, contains sections variously dating from February 1940 to October 1941.

Now, for a start, DZ203 needed new engines. It was fitted with an early civil version of the Pratt & Whitney Wasp, the S1H1-G driving a three-bladed, two-position variable-pitch propeller. By 1944, it was the only aircraft in the RAF or the USAAF in Britain, having this combination of Wasp engine and propeller, and the engines had probably exceeded the time between overhaul (TBO) which the UAL Maintenance Manual gives as 695 hours (see Appendix A). Furthermore, in addition to much work being required on the airframe, an American all-electric autopilot needed to be fitted, as well as installation of the electronic systems needed for the proposed automatic landing trials.

In February 1944 the Boeing 247-D was languishing at Defford, having being released at the end of its part in the X-band project. It was recorded in monthly returns as 'use of aircraft unsatisfactory, to be reviewed'.[107] The utilisation of the aircraft was indeed reviewed and the outcome was very much for the better as far as its proponents were concerned, with the decision to use the Boeing for the automatic landing trials. Griffiths did not wait for the intended refurbishment of DZ203, but was soon flying it again. On 7th March 1944, he took Lt Col Moseley on a round trip to Halton, Cheddington (a USAAF base) and Heston, returning to Defford. At the end of the month, he used the Boeing to fly with the two American officers (Capt Shauffacher and Lt Connor) to Bovingdon, where USAAF trials on SCS-51 were now based. Griffiths' last flight in the Boeing before it went for refurbishment, apart from two very short test flights on 8th and 9th June, was a trip to Speke with four airmen on board on 24th April, returning on the 26th with the same passengers.

One factor, relevant to the plans for refurbishment of DZ203 at this time, was that the USAAF in the United States had a small fleet of Boeing 247-Ds, which had been impressed into military service as the C-73. Their civil S1H1-G engines on impressment, were designated R-1340-53 by the US Army.[108] But these engines were progressively replaced in the C-73 fleet, by fitting military Wasp R-1340-AN-1 engines. Concurrently in the United States, C-73 aircraft were being used in conjunction with the Sperry Company for automatic landing trials at Wright Field.[109] No doubt this was known at Defford, and fitting the AN-1 variant of the Wasp, as used in vast numbers on the Harvard trainer, and its US service equivalents, AT-6 and SNJ, seemed an obvious move. But more was needed to get the old Boeing in good condition for its important task.

DZ203 was an American-built aircraft, which was to participate in a project of great interest to the Americans. Since Defford's Boeing needed refurbishment, so it may have been thought, where better to do it than in the United States?

On 17th May 1944, the British Air Commission (BAC) in Washington sent a cypher message to the Ministry of Aircraft Production (MAP), which was responsible for TRE, worded as follows:

'The Boeing 247 which is in use at Defford is we are told is in grave need of repair and you have no spares.
2. A.R.L. Wright Field would very much value the use of this aircraft in connection with their automatic blind landing experiments.
3. If you would ship it to the U.S.A., A.R.L. would have it reconditioned and fitted with automatic blind landing equipment, returning to you for demonstrating in due course, it being understood that they would have the use of the aircraft for two or three months before its return.
4. Agreement to this rather unusual request and prompt shipment of the aircraft would form a very practical gesture of appreciation to A.R.L. for their demonstration of the SCS-51 in U.K., and would improve goodwill between the experimental establishments'.

Although this message was almost certainly prompted by Moseley who was now back at Wright Field, it must have been received with mixed feelings at Defford, where it was recorded as received by TRE Registry on 23rd May 1944. On the one hand, it represented an opportunity to have DZ203 refurbished. On the other, TRE would be deprived of the use of an aircraft they valued highly, which would delay their development plans by at least three months. Also, the system being developed at Wright Field was not quite the one McDonald and TRE had in mind.

However, following a meeting at TFU on 5th June 1944, the Directorate of Communications Development (DCD) of the MAP at Harrogate, who had controlling authority over experimental flying at Defford, decided to accept this offer, and requested that the Boeing be despatched to Wright Field, asking for an estimated date and time of arrival in the United States.

This request was recorded as received at Defford on 19th June, and the work was put in hand to despatch the 247-D. It appears however, that it had travelled no further than Liverpool Docks (where it may have suffered some minor damage), when a further cypher arrived from BAC in Washington, which was received at Defford on 5th July, and in effect cancelled the movement.

The latest message said that the situation had altered since 17th May. American automatic landing development had been taken over by the Equipment Branch at Wright Field, with ARL (who had requested Defford's Boeing) now acting only in an advisory capacity. Furthermore, following the successful demonstrations in Britain by Col Moseley, *'...the RAF*[110] *had decided to fit twenty five B17s with the Moseley equipment, and these would be used to demonstrate automatic approach'* (This of course rather missed the point, since TRE wanted to use the Boeing 247-D to develop a fully automatic approach and landing system that included radar, with a distance measuring capability). But in a marked change of tone from the message of 17th May, BAC stated that under the circumstances it did not seem justifiable to ship the aircraft across the Atlantic and back again, not to mention the considerable effort involved in installing the autopilot equipment. However, at the end of the message came some encouragement for Defford:

'If you have an aircraft with A-5 or C-1 autopilot available, we should try to obtain the connecting units for you to complete the installation. Please confirm that this would be satisfactory'.

It appears that this is more or less what happened. The Boeing was returned to Defford, for the refurbishment to be carried out in Britain, and for an American electrical autopilot and the full automatic landing equipment to be installed. The Defford monthly returns for aircraft flying time[111] record nil hours for the Boeing in July, August and September 1944 – three months during which it was being largely rebuilt.

The MAP form 2101 record card for DZ203 shows that at the start of 1944, it was fitted with the same S1H1-G engines (identified as 5315 and 5316) with which it came from America in 1941, together with the propellers now listed as 279505 and 279506. On 28th July, engines 5315 and 5316 were sent to 24 MU Ternhill for overhaul, but this must only have served to confirm that these were beyond economic refurbishment. A requisition (AMA Y/22) was issued on 17th August for new engines, and replacement engines 327627 and 327744 were recorded as being fitted on 28th September 1944. These were ungeared Pratt & Whitney R-1340-AN-1 engines driving two-bladed Hamilton variable-pitch propellers, as fitted to the later marks of Harvard. They were drawn from Lend-Lease stocks, intended as spares for that trainer (1003 spare engines and 947 spare propellers for Harvards were supplied under Lend-Lease).

The installation of the new engines was completed by the middle of October, and on the 18th the Boeing was test flown by Gp Capt McDonald, with further air tests by McDonald and Griffiths on the 19th (landing by GCA) and 21st, these flights also involving Flt Lt Stewart, and Flt Lt Rogers (a specialist instrument engineer). By the end of October, a total of two hours had been flown with the new engines, and a further four were flown in November. Meanwhile, between test flights, work continued on the remaining refurbishment work on the Boeing, and the installation of equipment for the automatic landing trials.

Frank Griffiths wrote: *'When her original Wasp engines had worn themselves out, we found that no replacements were available, so we had installed two of the noisiest engines ever constructed. These were off Harvard aircraft. The propellers were ungeared and had only two angle of attack positions, fine and coarse. It was said that in fine pitch the tips of the propellers exceeded the speed of sound. The noise the Boeing made with two of these engines was quite extraordinary and distinctive, and I gloried in flying over Overbury village where Mac lived and where he would now be masticating his wartime breakfast of reconstituted powdered egg. He recognised the noise and it brought joy to his heart'.*

The monthly return from TFU Defford dated 2nd December 1944, confirms that the Boeing was now fitted with R-1340-AN-1 engines, although the aircraft continued to be listed as 'unserviceable' while other work continued.

Fitting the new engines had not been a simple task, as the necessary mountings had to be made individually by hand in the workshops at Defford. The overhaul also included a new system of undercarriage retraction – although intended as an improvement, this was not entirely successful because, as will be seen, there were further problems with this function.

The incorporation of the electric autopilot had to be a customised, one-of-a kind, installation. This was a major task in itself. Outside of the aircraft industry there was probably no other airfield in the UK where aeronautical design, manufacture and installation work, of the magnitude required for the Boeing, could be undertaken.

The personnel at Defford had learned a lot during their (often major) modification of aircraft to take large, complex, radar systems. Most

(Left) *The APU (Auxiliary Power Unit) installed in the Boeing by technicians and ground engineers at Defford, in what had been the luggage compartment (this offered 54 cu ft of capacity). An externally visible modification to DZ203 fitted at Defford, was the air intake for the APU seen to the left and above the open door to the luggage compartment, which was on the port side of the aircraft.* (Crown copyright via Sqn Ldr Mike Dean)

importantly, the Boeing was re-wired with a new 24 volt system, to meet the electrical demands of the automatic landing installation. A new APU was fitted in the rear luggage compartment and the aircraft was now fully equipped for night flying. The work bench described by Reg Batt, and the passenger seats, were removed from the passenger cabin (although most of the seats were soon reinstated). Gp Capt McDonald records that over 800 man-hours were spent at Defford reconditioning the Boeing, a great deal of the time being after normal working hours, such was the enthusiasm for the project.

The completed automatic landing trials installation in the Boeing, consisted of an American Minneapolis-Honeywell C-1 autopilot, operating on all three sets of control surfaces – rudder, elevators and ailerons. This was linked by a 'black box', based on that devised by Lt Col Francis Moseley, to an American SCS-51 instrument landing system, so that the aircraft was guided accurately along localiser and glide-path beams to bring it to the touch down point.

A murky but historic view of Boeing 247-D DZ203 at the culmination of an automatic approach in January 1945. (Crown copyright)

The crucial British contribution to the system in the Boeing was developed and built by Fg Off Leonard Barber at Defford. His 'black box' linked the autopilot to the Radar BA (BABS) system, which utilised a Rebecca interrogator in the nose of the Boeing, transmitting to a transponder beacon at the upwind end of the runway. The beacon was mobile, being mounted on a vehicle, and could be moved onto different runways according to wind direction. This was seen as an advance on the SCS-51 localiser, as it provided continuous information on range (which was not possible for the radio-technology based SCS-51 to provide), and operated out to a greater distance. Most importantly, the BABS range meter was visible to the pilot, and no longer on a cathode ray tube (CRT) display which was only for use by the navigator. Cockpit ergonomics were further improved by sending the directional information from the Radar BA through an improvised connection to a standard SCS-51 two-needle display which showed the pilot 'left-right' commands via the localiser needle, before the signal passed to the autopilot. However, a limitation of the British equipment was that it did not provide glide path information, so this still had to be derived from the American SCS-51 instrument landing system.[112]

The situation as seen by TRE in October 1944 was summarised in a report by Keith Wood, a TRE scientist who had been recruited at Bawdsey and worked under Bowen on airborne radar from 1937, which made the case for a radar based system and laid out a development programme which was subsequently followed.[113]

Griffiths suggests the autopilot and SCS-51 fitted to the Boeing came from one of the B-24 trials aircraft. He describes how it was coupled with the 'black box' developed by Moseley, and '... an automatic homing and orbiting device designed by a radar officer of unusual capability and potential. Flying Officer L C Barber was no ordinary radar officer. He had taken his degree in Chemistry at London University and I think research was in his blood, for he soon devised his own black box for smoothing out radar signals and feeding them into the autopilot so we could demonstrate 'hands off' flying to the airfield, orbiting at any given mileage, finding the landing beam and

136

(Above and below) *These photographs appear in Report TFU 70, dated January 1945, with a caption which reads:* 'The culmination of an automatic approach. This and the subsequent flying photographs were taken while the aircraft was actually under automatic control using the radar localiser system and the SCS-51 glide path'. *The photos show the very shallow ground angle of the Boeing close to the point of touch down.* (Crown copyright)

View from the cockpit of DZ203 during an automatic landing. The circular instrument immediately below the windscreen and just to the left of the central pillar is the Distance Meter, fed via 'Barber's Box'. Directly below this is the SCS-51 cross-pointer meter with horizontal and vertical needle indicators. (Crown Copyright)

then coming down the landing path in its own Boeing 247-D stately manner'.

Griffiths adds: *'Flight Sergeant Dolbear, a highly qualified electrician, had not only installed the Minneapolis Honeywell electric autopilot in the aircraft, but 'found' enough power for the electrics by installing a "chore horse" petrol engine driving a generator in the toilet compartment, exhausting through a hole cut in the side. Modern AID Inspectors would have had a fit...'*

The late Norman Dolbear described the fitting out of the Boeing and the trials as follows:

'A complete Honeywell autopilot was obtained, and together with all the associated equipment was fitted to the Boeing. Very thorough ground testing was followed by an air test which went very well. The next step was to carry out an auto approach. Accordingly we took off with Wing Commander Griffiths as pilot, Flying Officer Barber looking to the signals coming in, and myself keeping an eye on the autopilot. We flew over the Malvern Hills towards the Welsh Hills under autopilot control, then the auto-approach was selected. The Boeing turned gently around and settled on a course over the Malverns and towards the airfield. As the + pointer swung over, the approach beam was selected and a slow turn to port took us to face the runway. A gentle descent took us to the end of it and at about 50 ft or so the pilot reverted to manual control for a few seconds. This was done cautiously as he then gave it back to the auto and the Boeing settled down on the runway with a slightly heavier landing than with pilot control. Now was a time for glee as the trial had proved that an unsophisticated system such as we had worked, and deserved expansion'.[114]

On another occasion, writing in 2001, Norman Dolbear related how the interior of the 247-D had been modified.[115] In the cabin an obstruction was presented, as in all Boeing 247s, by the main spar carry-through structure. In DZ203 the cabin was further obstructed by a wooden box, enclosing the main gyro, mounted against the rear side of the main spar carry-through enclosure so as to be as central as possible. In the cockpit was a new main instrument panel which Dolbear had first modelled in cardboard for approval by Gp Capt McDonald and Wg Cdr Griffiths. The new panel, which now also accommodated the Minneapolis-Honeywell C-1 autopilot control unit, was then made from aluminium alloy by the Instrument Section at Defford using the cardboard mock-up as a template. Dolbear commented that it was fortunate there was no trouble with any of the instruments, as access to the rear of the panel was very limited, once it was in place.

The instrument panel of Boeing 247-D DZ203 when used for automatic landing trials, showing the range meter immediately above the cross pointer. (Crown copyright)

On 15th December 1944, Griffiths attended a meeting of the MAP Directors' (R & D) Committee Technical Advisory Panel No. 3, and reported that the Boeing was ready for flight trials with the automatic landing system. He also reported on American trials with SCS-51 (now referred to as ABL-10) conversions at the USAAF base at Watton in Norfolk. Of fifteen ABL-10 units constructed, ten had been fitted to B-17s for trials, and four to B-24s, while the fifteenth conversion unit had been loaned to TRE and installed in the Boeing.

On 16th December at Defford, Gp Capt McDonald was airborne at the controls of DZ203 for a 40 minute flight, in a demonstration to AVM Tait (Director General of Signals), accompanied by Sqn Ldr Proctor (2nd pilot), Fg Off Barber and Fg Off Rogers. Three days later, Griffiths flew for one hour testing the automatic approach system, accompanied by Proctor, Barber and Dolbear. It is recorded that the Boeing flew a total of five hours in December, and on the 30th of the

A view taken looking up at the ceiling of the cockpit of DZ203, showing the autopilot control panel (top centre), also the orbit range selector below, just above the compass. (Crown copyright)

month it was being equipped with new radio channels described as being the same as on Oxford NM599.

In the first two weeks of January 1945, the Boeing was flown intensively by Griffiths, on what his flying log book describes as 'auto approach' work, usually with Stewart as his co-pilot, and accompanied by Barber. On 10th January, Griffiths and Stewart had a cabin full of TRE scientists (Holt-Smith, Birch, Baldwin and Powell) for an SCS-51 demonstration flight lasting one hour.

On the 16th January, the MAP Directors' (R & D) Committee Technical Advisory Panel No. 3 held their meeting at Defford, where

A view looking forward inside the cabin of DZ203, showing the complete radar installation for automatic landing trials on the left, with the autopilot junction box on the right. The cabin was obstructed by the main spar carry-through, seen lower centre, and the aft step-over has been replaced with the box housing the main gyro. A number of other features of this 247-D as it was in 1945 can be seen, with one retained passenger seats on the left. (Crown copyright)

as the minutes record, TFU reported on flights with SCS-51, Minneapolis-Honeywell autopilot and Moseley coupling box, together with Radar BA coupled to the autopilot by 'Barber's Box'. McDonald and Griffiths evidently decided they were sufficiently confident in the system to give a full demonstration to the assembled scientists and senior officers. In Griffiths' words: *'Invitations were sent out to all who should be indoctrinated to come to Defford and see a practical demonstration of Automatic Landing actually working'*. The outcome was memorable.

The cabin of DZ203 in early January 1945, looking aft, with the radar installation for automatic landings on the right of the picture. This photograph shows well the main spar carry-through in the foreground, with step-over, and the enclosure for the main gyro immediately behind. Also to be seen are some surviving features of the Boeing's days as an airliner – the patterned wall covering over sound and thermal insulation, curtains, ashtrays, and the tip-up jump seat for the stewardess on the door in the rear cabin bulkhead. Above this is a plaque recording, probably erroneously, that DZ203 reached a total of 10,000 flying hours in April 1944. The passenger door on the starboard side at the rear of the cabin, which is recessed in the thickness of the wall panelling so cannot be seen from this view, reveals itself by the splash of sunlight on the aft bulkhead coming through the window in the door. The missing passenger seats were very soon replaced, as in January 1945 and thereafter, the Boeing regularly flew carrying up to 8 passengers. (Crown copyright via Sqn Ldr Mike Dean)

On that day, 16th January 1945, Boeing 247-D DZ203, flown by Wg Cdr Frank Griffiths with Flt Lt Stewart as his co-pilot, and with 'Members of the Auto Approach Panel' as passengers, made what is recorded as the world's first Automatic Landing following an automatic orbit and approach. Griffiths' log book triumphantly notes this as 'THE demonstration … First Auto Landing!'

In a letter to 'Flight International' magazine in 1964 headed 'The First Automatic Landing', Gp Capt McDonald credits Stewart with being at the controls on this occasion, and comments: 'Moseley, Stewart and Barber were a rare combination of experts in instrument flying and electronics'.[116] Oddly enough, in this letter, which gives some precise data on the Boeing and its equipment, but is otherwise written in a rather casual and off-the-cuff style, McDonald states that the first automatic landing in the Boeing was in October 1944, and this date has been widely quoted. However, this cannot be so. Towards the end of October 1944, the Boeing had only just flown again after its rebuild, and had yet to have all the automatic landing equipment installed, work which was not completed until December 1944.

Frank Griffiths later commented on the Boeing: *'Because it was flapless and had a very low approach angle it could land without 'flare out'. I think it was the only aircraft which could do this in Europe at the time and this was a feature of the aircraft design, not of its landing system. It could be brought in "over the hedge" at 55 knots. We were just lucky to have the placid Boeing'.*

After the successful demonstration of automatic landing in daylight, Griffiths was keen to move on quickly to prove the system by landing the Boeing in fog or at night. He records: *'Stewart and I had her fitted up with a blind flying hood for the first pilot, and we became confident at bringing her in on automatics completely blind with whoever was safety pilot sitting in the co-pilot's seat to check visually. We would have liked to do a fog landing but of course the fog would not oblige. So we hit on the idea of carrying out a completely automatic landing at night without lights. It was easy to arrange as blackout restrictions were still enforced (in January 1945).*

'This idea turned into a humiliating fiasco and really impressed me with the difficulty of overcoming man's natural instincts. We clambered into the sky on that moonless January night fully confident of our ability to home automatically from a distance, orbit the airfield and come sedately down the approach beam in the normal Boeing manner. A rumble of the wheels on the runway would be the first that we would know that we had arrived.

'It was not to be. When the radio altimeter read 100 feet above the ground my nerves wouldn't stand the twitch any longer. I just had to switch on the wing landing lights only to find, as usual, we were exactly where we should be and the runway was straight ahead'.[117]

Griffiths' log book records this flight as being on 21st January 1945, with the added comment *'Auto orbiting and auto approach at night. One auto landing – no lights'*.

There were four passengers in the aircraft on that night – Flt Lt Rogers, Fg Off Clarke, WO Palmer and LAC Moore. Their feelings are not recorded.

Notes arising from the Technical Advisory Panel No. 3 meeting held on 16th January record that by this date, the Boeing had flown 10 hours 50 minutes on auto approaches, using (a) SCS-51, and (b) Radar BA (BABS) in conjunction with Rebecca Mk II. Twenty-seven approaches used the SCS-51 localiser, and 17 the Radar BA; all were satisfactory apart from some oscillations in the glide path, which needed further research.

McDonald explained the distinction between the methods tested when he later wrote: *'At this early stage the object of the trials was (a) to try to reproduce in our Boeing, the results the Americans had already obtained on 8th Air Force aircraft, and (b) to endeavour to substitute British radar for the American localiser system as a means of operating the autopilot. On the aerodrome the ground layout was the standard American SCS-51 pattern of VHF localiser and glide path, plus a BABS localiser transponder-beacon operating on 219 Mc/s (Receive) and 224 Mc/s (Transmit).*

'In the Boeing, switching arrangements enabled the pilot to select at will:

1. *SCS-51*
2. *Radar Beam Approach*
3. *Radar Beam Approach plus American glide path.*

Fg Off Barber designed and manufactured a special unit which enabled the radar system to tie up with the American system by feeding pulses from the Rebecca through a conversion unit to a pilot's distance indicator and thence through the Moseley connector box to the automatic pilot. In this way it was possible to feed the auto-system either from the American VHF SCS-51 system or the British radar system, and to compare the two'.

The next stage was to demonstrate automatic homing and orbiting, in order to meet the requirement for a rapid landing system for aircraft returning from operations at night and in all weathers.[118] This was achieved by installing a modified Rebecca set with vertically polarised aerials, designed by Fg Off Barber, in the wooden nose compartment of the Boeing. The aerials were separated from each other by a metal screen and isolated from the rest of the aircraft by a metal bulkhead that acted as a reflector, and a Eureka ground beacon of increased power was erected on the airfield control tower. This enabled the Boeing, flying at 3,000 feet, to home reliably from 50 miles, and then orbit the airfield, before making an approach and landing, all under automatic control. During these manoeuvres, the pilot had only to monitor the system and make throttle adjustments as necessary. McDonald observed: *'From the pilot's point of view, accurate orbiting of the airfield, especially in overcast and cloud conditions, calls for great flying skill and accuracy, and is difficult in a strong wind. The combination of the radar-based system, "Barber's box" and the autopilot, offered the opportunity to set the aircraft to orbit automatically at a set distance from the airfield, so that the aircraft could orbit and land entirely automatically. A special*

Equipment fitted to Boeing 247-D DZ203 for automatic landing trials, January 1945.

Above: *The approach control switch, which was mounted on the left hand side of the auto pilot control panel above the compass.*

Below: *The SCS installation showing on the right, the localiser receiver, in the centre, the glide path receiver, and on the left the marker receiver.* (Crown copyright)

Eureka beacon for this purpose was set up in the control tower at Defford, so the pilot could set the orbit range at will from between 1 to 10 miles, holding the aircraft at a constant range in orbit. This was checked against the SCS-51 localiser and found to be accurate and worked well'.

What Griffiths had described as a 'fiasco', when first attempting an automatic landing at night, was in fact far from it, and this technique, combined with automatic homing, was soon proven by the Boeing. McDonald is quite clear in his recollection: *'The Boeing was thus the first aircraft ever to fly on an automatic orbit of the airfield. On one occasion the pilot orbited the airfield and landed off the orbit entirely on automatic control and in complete darkness'.*

Fg Off Barber, evidently with the full encouragement of the Air Ministry, filed a British patent application to cover his invention, *'Improvements in and relating to radio control systems for aircraft and other vehicles'*, in September 1945.[119] The Ministry of Supply filed a similar patent in the United States in 1947, and Barber was later awarded £200 by the Committee of Awards to Inventors, which had been set up after the war.[120]

During February 1945, the Boeing completed over 20 hours trials flying involving a further 34 automatic approaches, frequently piloted by McDonald, Griffiths and Stewart. The fact that the Station Commander (McDonald) and the Officer Commanding Flying (Griffiths) were so often at the controls of the Boeing emphasises the importance of these trials and the interest which they engendered. On the 20th February, AVM 'Pathfinder' Bennett (OC of No 8 Group) was an interested observer on board the Boeing, accompanied by Barber and with McDonald and Stewart at the controls. Bennett was already well known at Defford as he had made many technical visits there following up on progress with radar system development for the Pathfinder Force.

Trials with the Boeing continued to go well, and at the March meeting of the Technical Advisory Panel, McDonald was able to report the aircraft had now completed 70 hours of flying, and the autopilot, Rebecca Mk II and the SCS-51 were proving reliable.

Equipment fitted to Boeing 247-D DZ203 for automatic landing trials, January 1945.
Above: *A close up view in the cabin looking aft, showing the radar installation, with the 'Barber' conversion box the rearmost of the three units shown.*
Below: *This photo in Report TFU 70 was captioned:* 'Another view of the Radar Installation and the Conversion Box'. (Crown copyright)

It was reported: '... *the Boeing has arrived over the runway and landed in conditions which would only have been possible with the finest manual flying'.*[121] At this meeting it was agreed to fit the modified Rebecca (Mark VI) for homing from a greater distance, as part of what was described as the 'Ritson conversion' to the Boeing. This work was carried out between 3rd and 9th April, during which time a full inspection of the aircraft was completed. (Dr. F J U Ritson was a TRE scientist[122], who was frequently present on flights in the Boeing on automatic landing trials in May and June 1945, no doubt working on the modified system which carried his name). Despite the clear attribution to Dr Ritson, McDonald gives credit mainly to Barber for devising and progressively improving the homing element of the system in the Boeing and on the ground.

Attempts were then made to reproduce the success of the Boeing, using SCS-51coupled to a Minneapolis-Honeywell autopilot fitted in a Lancaster. According to McDonald: *'The Lancaster was heavily flapped, and designed to accept a reasonably steep descent of up to 5 or even 6 degrees, with a fairly violent change of attitude at flare-out. This, of course, was not at all suited to auto-approach ...'*[123]

At first sight this recollection, some years after the event, appears to differ from the findings of TFU Report No. 77, dated March 1945, and signed by McDonald, which concluded:

'Given good localiser and glide path beam it is considered that a Lancaster aircraft fitted with Minneapolis-Honeywell autopilot, Moseley Coupling unit and SCS-51, is capable of carrying out satisfactory automatic approaches down to a height of 150 feet with consistency and reliability, the approach being better than that of an average pilot flying manually'.[124]

However, there is no inconsistency if one notes that McDonald in his recollections about automatic landing as a whole, regularly used the phrase 'auto-approach' to embrace both automatic approach and automatic landing including touch-down, while TFU Report No. 77 was only about the automatic approach, down to 150 feet.

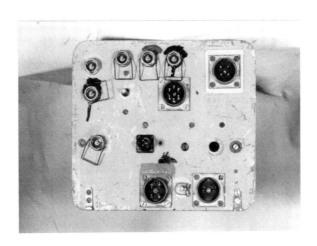

'Barber's Box'. *This unit was designed and built by Fg Off L. C. Barber. It enabled the radar approach system to tie up with the US SCS-51 system by feeding pulses from the Rebecca receiver to the pilot's distance indicator, and thence through the Moseley connector box to the automatic pilot.*

Above: *The front panel, showing the switching system, and connections to SCS-51 (top right) and radar range meter (bottom right).*

Below: *Behind the front panel.* (Crown copyright)

So while the automatic control system tested on the Boeing may have been transferrable to other aircraft types in the approach configuration, transition through to touchdown was another matter. The Boeing was unusual insofar as it had a low wing loading, and hence a low approach speed, which gave a low rate of descent when a shallow approach was flown. Indeed, photographs of automatic landing trials at Defford show the aircraft in a virtually flat attitude immediately prior to touching down. This enabled a 'hands-off' landing to be achieved at the end of an automatic approach. A higher approach speed, as in the case of the Lancaster, for a given glide path angle, meant a higher rate of descent, which needed to be reduced to an acceptable level before touchdown. For any tail-wheel aircraft, a 'wheeler' landing (i.e. main-wheels contacting the runway first), at a high rate of descent, is likely to result in the aircraft rapidly becoming airborne again. This happens as the tail drops, thus increasing the wing's angle of attack and giving more lift momentarily. In the case of a nose-wheel aircraft, a firm touchdown on the main-wheels will cause the aircraft to pitch forward onto the nose-wheel, reducing the angle of attack of the wing and hence lift – in this instance the aircraft will tend to stay on the ground.

Gp Capt McDonald therefore made the case for nose-wheel undercarriage clear to the British civil aviation industry, if advantage were to be taken of the automatic landing system, but he felt manufacturers were slow to respond. (Unlike their American counterparts, British airliners in the immediate post-war period were generally tail-wheel types, e.g. York, Hermes I, Tudor, Viking, as were all British bombers at that time).

TFU Report No. 77 on the first trials of automatic approach on a Lancaster concluded by commenting: *'Flying on auto-pilot near the ground inevitably involves a certain amount of risk especially during early trials of this sort, and it is desired to place on record the names of those who took part. Pilots – Wg Cdr F.C. Griffiths, assisted by Flt Lt K.B. Hollowell and Gp Capt J.A. McDonald. Technicians – Flt Lt J. Rogers (Instruments), Flt Lt L.C. Barber (Signals)'.*

McDonald recalled: *'The Boeing was ... steady on a 3 degree glide path, except for kinks in the glide path beam caused by minor local obstructions (and a railway). Although hardly noticeable on manual flying, these were very frightening on auto-approach ... The Lancaster, even at about 40 degrees flap, yawed a great deal on auto-approach; while at full flap the pull on the control surfaces was so great the trials were abandoned.'*

These concerns are not mentioned in TFU Report No. 77, and perhaps reflect different attitudes to flying safety in wartime, and in peace. By 1960 when he recorded his reminiscences, McDonald was retiring from the post of Deputy Commandant of London Heathrow Airport, one of the most responsible civil aviation posts in the world. No doubt he shuddered at the risks he and his colleagues took, and expected of others, during the war.

From TFU Report No. 77 quoted above, it will be seen that a new name had joined the select group of pilots who were flying automatic landing trials at Defford. Flt Lt Kenneth Hollowell had his first experience of the Boeing, as second pilot to Flt Lt Stewart on 15th March 1945, on a beam approach trial. This was followed by two more flights on 21st March, also as second pilot to Stewart, on automatic approach using only SCS-51, before taking over the left-hand seat with Stewart as second pilot for a third trial on that day. Thereafter, Hollowell piloted the Boeing frequently as trials and demonstrations progressed, while DZ203 is listed less often by McDonald and Griffiths in their flying log books during this period.

The 10th of April was the date set for the next meeting of the Technical Advisory Panel, which was due to be attended by a larger than usual number of influential people. Gp Capt McDonald decided to use the occasion to demonstrate the full range of automatic landing capabilities of the Boeing to this important audience.

But the day before, 9th April 1945, the Boeing was involved in an incident which is described in his inimitable style by Frank Griffiths, who was a wonderful story teller and a most entertaining writer, in his book 'Angel Visits'. He wrote in 1986: *'On this glorious spring day with a light easterly wind, I took off for a final air test of the automatic homing and landing equipment. My crew consisted of Figaro Barber and Flight Sergeant Dolbear...*

All went well as we cruised round the Vale of Evesham admiring the blossoming apple trees... She was homing herself back to the airfield prior to coming in to land on the automatics. I selected wheels down for the undercarriage and when it was half-way down it jammed!

'*I took control from the autopilot and cruised around still unconcerned. We'd had problems like this before. But this time there was no sorting it out; Figaro and Dolbear tried to get the wheels down using the emergency manual system. Nothing happened. It was jammed solid, in the half way down position ... (but) if I could land her with the undercarriage half down and if the propellers didn't touch the ground and if she didn't go on her nose, we could still save the day for the demonstration on the morrow... It was to show George Gardner, Head of a Department at* (and subsequently Director of) *RAE Farnborough, just what the Boeing could do. We expected him to be critical of our idea, for we had already proved that Moseley's system had to be used with an electric autopilot and Gardner had designed the remarkable 'huff and puff' Mark VIII autopilot. It was a compressed air autopilot which was nowhere near accurate enough for our purpose. Obviously the designer of the Mark VIII autopilot would not like to be told that his baby wasn't up to the job'.*

Griffiths goes on to describe the preparation for and execution of a skilled emergency landing on the grass. But at the end of an otherwise successful landing, the aircraft gently tipped up onto its nose.

'*It didn't look too bad. Just the nose crushed in a bit. Then I noticed a clod of earth on the tip of the port propeller. If the plumbers (ground engineers) saw that it would mean an engine change. If a propeller ever struck the ground or any object it was a golden rule the engine must be changed in case internal damage had occurred. I knew it hadn't – the ground was very soft – so I quickly knocked the clod off the propeller tip and polished it with my handkerchief, rotating it until it was horizontal like the starboard prop! Then with my foot I pressed flat a few divots cut up by the spinning prop and awaited the arrival of the plumbers'.*

Frank Griffiths describes how the technical staff worked through the night, laying strips of thin plywood over the broken nose, gluing and drying with hair dryers borrowed from the WAAF's quarters. The Boeing was lifted onto its wheels and the undercarriage locked down. The demonstration went ahead, it was a great success, and Dr. Gardner was suitably impressed.

However, inspection of the pilots' flying log books, while consistent with most of the above, shows a slightly different story. Kenneth Hollowell's log book shows that it was he who was flying the Boeing on 9th April, accompanied by Flt Lt Clarke and Fg Off Barber, when there was *'trouble with the U/C – landed OK on nose – 1.25 hrs'*. Griffiths did fly the Boeing on 9th April, presumably prior to Hollowell's fateful flight, when he (Griffiths) was accompanied by Barber and Dolbear, on an 'E&A' (engines and airframe) test. Prior to that, on the same date, there was also a flight piloted by Hollowell together with Griffiths, Barber and Dolbear on an 'auto-pilot, homing and approach trial, 0.55 hrs', but again with no mention of undercarriage problems.

A likely explanation for the discrepancy is that Griffiths took on his shoulders responsibility for the actions of his subordinate Hollowell. Griffiths too had experience with malfunction of the undercarriage of the Boeing, which may have been imprinted on his mind, and over the years the two stories probably became fused as one.

In fact, this was definitely not the end of problems with the Boeing's undercarriage. On 11th May 1945, Hollowell recorded in his log book a flight with four passengers on board for a demonstration flight: *'U/C trouble, not down to full extent'*. In 1946, when an engineer and a photographer from Boeing visited Defford, it was reported that the 247-D was now flown with the undercarriage locked down permanently.[125]

A minor mystery from this time is that photographs of the Boeing taken in 1945, very clearly show quite prominent bulges, one on each of the engine cowlings. The bulges are 'handed' as seen from the front, in that on the starboard cowling the bulge is at 'one o'clock', while that on the port side is at 'eleven o'clock' – that is to say they are inclined in towards the fuselage. The bulges do not seem to be

*The Servicing Group responsible for the Boeing 247-D during the historic automatic landing trials at Defford. The original print of the photograph is annotated on the reverse, '*Taken on 17th September 1945 at request of Officer Commanding Servicing Wing'. *This photo was taken after the landing incident described by Frank Griffiths – the temporary repairs to the nose of DZ203 can be seen, where strips of plywood have been glued over the damaged area. The photo also shows the unexplained 'handed' bulges on the engine cowlings mentioned in the text. The aircraft behind is another Boeing – a B-17.* (Crown copyright)

related to any engine function. Similar bulges have not been seen on any aircraft of the Harvard type (when the engines were drawn from Harvard stock, they presumably came with their cowlings) or any member of the Harvard's extended family. The purpose of these bulges remains unknown. Shaun Pocock, today a member of the RAF Defford Reunion Association, who served at Defford as an Instrument Technician in 1946, suggests they represent some local sheet metal work, a 'mod' to the cowling related to the radar test function of the Boeing, possibly to prevent interference from the engines or propellers, or perhaps to house electrical generators or hydraulic pumps. There may be a clue in the report to the Panel on 16th January 1945, which stated that with radar controlled blind approach, there was a problem related to *'...the need to get rid of propeller modulation and local interference'.*[126]

Many years later, McDonald wrote summarising the trials which had taken place in early 1945: *'We were able to home the Boeing from 50 miles range, orbit the airfield at a selected range, line up with the runway and land, all on the auto-approach system – results not previously achieved in any sphere of aviation at that time'.*[127] This is undoubtedly true, as is the claim of the world's first automatic landing in 1945, albeit as McDonald noted: *'During these manoeuvres under auto control the pilot monitors the system and makes throttle adjustments as necessary'.* While the autopilot on the Boeing controlled all three flight surfaces, throttle control, an essential

Members of the team who worked with the Boeing 247-D DZ203 on automatic landing in 1945. Left to right: LAC Atkinson, Flt Sgt Squirrell, Cpl Cusworth, LAC Scanlan, Fg Off L.C. Barber, Flt Lt K.C. Hollowell, Flt Lt J. Rogers, Wg Cdr F.C. Griffiths, Gp Capt J.A. McDonald, Flt Sgt Dolbear, Sgt Burningham, Flt Sgt Elliott, Cpl Potter, Cpl Harman, LAC Reason, LAC Finch, Sgt Hayes. (Crown copyright)

element in aircraft landing, had to await the outcome of a chain of post-war development through the Blind Landing Experimental Unit and Smiths Industries which resulted in the system of automatic landing introduced into commercial service by the Trident in 1964.

By the end of May 1945, although the War in Europe was over, trials with the Boeing continued with some intensity. But in the words of Gp Capt McDonald: *'The need for an accurate bad weather landing system for bombers was no longer of vital urgency. The scientists at TRE Malvern were anxious to get back to their universities, to face the tremendous task of educational reconstruction. The skilled radar and aircraft technicians at Defford were keen to get back to "civvie street" before all the good jobs were swallowed up'.* The future now lay in civil aviation, where the pioneering work with the Boeing at Defford was seen, quite correctly, as being of enormous importance for the safe and efficient operation of air transport.

As early as 28th February 1945, Griffiths had piloted the Boeing on a demonstration flight recorded as an 'auto demonstration for civil aviation' with Air Cdre Dean and a Mr Collins on board as passengers. This was a sign of things to come.

From 29th July to 2nd August 1945, the 3rd CERCA conference (a gathering of 60 delegates from the Commonwealth concerned with aviation electronics) was held at TRE Malvern and Defford, with Britain, Australia, Canada, India, Newfoundland, New Zealand, South Africa, Southern Rhodesia and the USA, plus the British Colonial Office, all represented.[128]

Notable among the delegates were Viscount Swinton, who had been Secretary of State for Air during the formative years of radar, Sir Robert Watson-Watt ('the Father of Radar') and Lt Col Moseley, who might with some justice have claimed to be the father of automatic landing. The programme included a comprehensive demonstration of automatic landing by the Boeing using combinations of SCS-51 with the Moseley coupling; Rebecca and the Barber Conversion Unit; and all combined to give automatic homing, orbiting, approach and landing. On demonstrations for the CERCA delegates, over the three

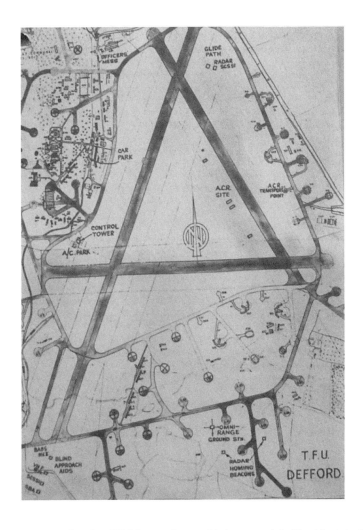

The programme for the CERCA meeting at Malvern and Defford in July 1945, which was issued to delegates, included this plan of Defford Airfield. It shows the position of BABS Mk II, VHF, SCS-51 and SBA installations at the southern end of the main runway 01/09, with BABS Mk II and SCS-51 at the northern approach end, and radar homing beacons offset from 01/19 on the south east side of the airfield. The airfield plan also shows the location of the Aircraft Park, the Car Park and (on a knoll overlooking Croome Court) the Officers' Mess for refreshments. (Crown copyright)

days 30th and 31st July, and 1st August, Griffiths recorded a total of seven and half hours flying time on the Boeing. On 31st July, Griffiths flew to Northolt in the Boeing to collect Viscount Swinton and his party personally[129], arriving back at Defford by 'auto-landing'. McDonald too was involved with demonstrations of the Boeing for CERCA delegates, with three Boeing flights on 31st July.

The determination to 'sell' automatic landing to the civil aviation industry continued. On the day after the last of the demonstrations to the CERCA conference, 2nd August 1945, Griffiths gave the same demonstration as for CERCA, to a full passenger-load of Senior Officers from RAF Transport Command, many of whom would be expecting to go on to post-war careers with the airlines.

The Boeing continued to be employed on trials and demonstrations related to 'automatic homing, orbit and landing' throughout 1945 and into 1946. We know of four pilots who flew the Boeing intensively during this period, because their flying log books have survived – John McDonald, Frank Griffiths, Kenneth Hollowell and (in the autumn of 1946) Eric Knowles. No doubt the Boeing was flown many times by other pilots, whose log books have not survived or not been seen, but those of the four pilots named probably give a representative view of the flying duties carried out.

The log books of Wg Cdr J M Southwell, Sqn Ldr J C Thelwell and Flt Lt E W Arnott have survived but these officers only flew (as pilot or 2nd pilot) in the Boeing on a few occasions. However, from surviving log books, where the names of both pilot and 2nd pilot are recorded, it is possible to identify a number of others who piloted the Boeing during this period, in particular Sqn Ldr (formerly Flt Lt) Stewart, who played an important part in the first auto landing trials, and Sqn Ldr Allies, who flew the Boeing on a number of occasions, including an air test on 12th September 1945 with Flt Lt W E P Webb. Other known pilots of the Boeing in this period include Sqn Ldr Annis, Flt Lt Johnson, and Flt Lt Ellis. Of these only the flying log book of Flt Lt Webb appears to have survived.[130]

In the two years from the first flight of the Boeing after refurbishment in October 1944 until it was withdrawn from use in late 1946, Gp

Capt John McDonald piloted DZ203 on 63 occasions, flying a total of 58 hours.

Wg Cdr Frank Griffiths, who had also flown the Boeing quite extensively from Christchurch, Hurn and Defford in his first tour with TFU 1941-1943, recorded a further 47 hours on 49 flights in the Boeing in 1944 and 1945, between the first test flights in October 1944 after fitting new engines, and his departure from Defford in September 1945, plus a few more flights in his capacity of RAF Commanding Officer of the Blind Landing Experimental Unit at Woodbridge. In this post, he had his last flight in the Boeing in November 1945, having been the first to fly it in England on 2nd August 1941.

The third of the four pilots known to have flown the Boeing many times during the automatic landing project, was Flt Lt Kenneth Hollowell AFC. He joined the RAFVR in January 1938, and had an early introduction to AI radar in action when he flew first Blenheims, then Beaufighters, with 25 Squadron during 1940 and 1941, shooting down four enemy bombers, while claiming two 'probables' and others damaged. He left for the Middle East in February 1942, where amongst other duties, he test flew freshly assembled Lend-Lease aircraft at Takoradi in West Africa. So he arrived at Defford in December 1944 with practical combat experience of radar and good credentials as a test pilot. His first experience on the Boeing was on 15th March 1945, as second pilot to Stewart, after which he flew it regularly, especially in the period May to September 1945, recording 67 hours on 87 flights.

After Hollowell left Defford to become an Air Traffic Controller in Africa, and with Griffiths posted away, Gp Capt McDonald stepped up the number of hours he flew trials and demonstrations in the Boeing, which continued up to January 1946. From that date, little is known of how many flights the Boeing made and who its pilots were, except there are occasional records of flights in the hands of McDonald, Allies, Southwell, Ellis and Johnson. The flying log books of McDonald, Griffiths and Hollowell show that these three pilots (plus no doubt many others), piloted the Boeing intensively

(Left) *Flight Lieutenant Keith Hollowell AFC, who frequently piloted the Boeing on automatic landing trials in 1945.* (Mrs. Lindsay Corr)

throughout the rest of 1945. There were so many flights by these three that it would be repetitive and cumbersome to refer to them all. Some of the flights were tests and trials but more than half were demonstrations of automatic landing to distinguished and influential visitors.

Senior RAF officers, including Air Marshal Sir Edgar Ludlow-Hewitt (Inspector-General of the RAF), came to Defford in dozens. There were visits by senior civil servants and Government scientists, notable amongst them Sir Robert (later Lord) Renwick[131], who came to see the outcome of the project he had initiated. Officers of the US 8th Air Force and various American establishments were well represented, and two Russian Army officers (who were visiting TRE in Malvern), came to Defford on 31st August 1945, when Griffiths took them for a demonstration flight in the Boeing. AVM Don Bennett, soon to be Chief Executive of British South American Airways, made more than one visit for a demonstration flight in the Boeing, while a close observer who also would have seen the commercial possibilities of automatic landing was Lt Cdr Milward, OC Naval Section at Defford, later to become Sir Anthony Milward OBE, Chairman of British European Airways.

The instrument panel of Lancaster I PD438, used for the automatic approach and landing trials described in TFU Report No. 77, showing the position of the 'Radar BA' distance meter and the SCS51 cross-pointer. (Crown copyright)

On 25th August 1945, Lt Col Moseley was back at Defford to see what had been achieved. He flew in the Boeing and gave the project his blessing. He was presented with an inscribed Defford unit crest, which John McDonald heard later was displayed prominently in his office in the United States.

Some months earlier, on 21st April 1945, Frank Brady together with Lt Connor, who had piloted the early trials of the B-24 with SCS-51, had been welcomed as visitors to Defford. Griffiths and Barber gave Brady and Connor a comprehensive demonstration in the Boeing, having collected them from Bovingdon. The visits and demonstrations continued for the rest of 1945 and into 1946, with the emphasis continuing to be on civil applications. For the moment the future of the Boeing seemed assured, following a review of the aircraft establishment at Defford, as the MAP Form 2101 record card for DZ203 carried the entry dated 19th December 1945: *'Retention approved for use as a Flying Laboratory'*.

Defford airfield in 1946, at the time of the PICAO demonstrations. (Dennis Williams)

9. PICAO SWANSONG

Through the early months of 1946 the Boeing automatic landing trials continued at Defford, especially testing, proving and demonstrating homing and orbiting at a longer range with the latest version of Rebecca. The veteran airman and pioneer of flight refuelling, Sir Alan Cobham, was a distinguished visitor who enjoyed a demonstration flight with Gp Capt McDonald in the Boeing on 7th January 1946. The Boeing also visited RAE Farnborough on several occasions during this period.

During 1946, the very strict security at Defford relaxed a little. Fred Baker, a Boeing service engineer, visited the TFU to inspect the Boeing. He was accompanied by a photographer, Vern Manion who took a fine set of photographs, which are now in the Boeing corporate archives in Seattle. The photos show Fred Baker, in US military uniform, discussing maintenance of the Boeing with RAF personnel. Judging by the clear sky above, the brightness of the light, the shortness of the shadows and the airmen in shirt sleeves, the photos were most likely taken during the summer of 1946. Manion was probably on an extended tour of Europe, almost certainly travelling from and to the United States by ship. According to the Boeing archives, the photographs were not credited to Manion until 27th January 1947. A selection of the photos duly appeared in the February 1947 edition of the house magazine, 'Boeing News', accompanied by a story headed 'KING-SIZE JOB':

' "Old No. 1726" was one of the world's most advanced-type transports when it left the factory in the summer of 1933. As a member of the Boeing 247 family, it was to play a leading role in the development of modern air transportation. Going on fourteen now, the elderly plane is still up to its wing-tips in development work. Despite its age and its number of flying hours – almost 12,000 – the plane was specially selected by England's Royal Air Force for testing of modern radio, radar, electronics and navigational aids. Modified, but still a Boeing, the 247-D is stationed at Defford, Worcestershire, in the RAF's Telecommunications Flying Unit. Experiments involve

DZ203 at Defford, 1946. This and the photos in the series which follows, were taken by Vern Manion, a Boeing photographer. In the Boeing Magazine for February 1947, the caption to the photo below reads: 'Fred Baker, Boeing service engineer who ran across "Old 1726" at Defford, inspects new power plant RAF installed'. (The Boeing Company)

In the article in the corporate magazine 'Boeing News' for February 1947, the photograph above *was captioned:* 'The 247, whose type was the forerunner of modern commercial transports, now carries electronic equipment. RAF feel the plane is well suited for job and good for many more hours'. *Sadly, within a few months of this photo being taken, the Boeing was withdrawn from use and condemned to scrap.* (The Boeing Company)

the study of remotely-controlled take-off and landing with autopilots, blind landing beams and other high-frequency radio installations.

'*According to British flyers working with the Boeing, the ship was selected for this work because of its ruggedness, reliability, and excellent stability characteristics*'.

Meanwhile trials and demonstrations of auto-landing with the Boeing continued at Defford.

As John McDonald saw so clearly, in the post-war era, the future of much radar development, and of automatic landing in particular, lay with civil aviation. So it proved. During the immediate post-war period, in the words of Reg Batt:

'*One of the most important tasks for TRE was to adapt wartime radar, particularly centimetre radar, to the needs of civil aviation. The person best equipped to lead the development of radar for civil aviation was John Duckworth, whose division at TRE had already been concerned with airfields and air traffic control problems during the war. The summit of their achievement had been the mighty AMES 70 system. The techniques of this and other similar systems developed for the RAF were readily adaptable for civil use, but a degree of international co-operation was essential. Accordingly, PICAO – the Provisional International Civil Aviation Organisation[132] – was set up to co-ordinate the development of navigational systems, air-traffic control measures and fare structure on a world-wide basis... With the United States, Britain was in the van of this burgeoning movement*'.

As the AMES radar technology was developed for civil air traffic control, the arc-shaped scanners of this type of system soon became a familiar sight at airports across the world. At the time that this surveillance radar was finding its civil application[133], it was also inevitable with Gp Capt McDonald in charge at Defford, that automatic landing would also remain high on the agenda for PICAO. First of all though, during July 1946, there was a series of demonstrations of automatic landing, to civil aviation visitors, including representatives from the British state-owned airlines, from

Fred Baker (centre), a Boeing service engineer in uniform, with two unidentified RAF officers at Defford. The 'temporary' repairs to the nose of DZ203, effected in April 1945, can still be seen in the summer of 1946. On the reverse of the original print of this photo by Boeing photographer Vern Manion, is written 'Ship now flown with undercarriage gear locked down'. (The Boeing Company)

BOAC, BEA and BSAA; and groups representing airline crews - the Guild of Air Pilots & Air Navigators (GAPAN), the British Air Line Pilots' Association (BALPA) and the Radio Operators' Union.

These demonstrations were followed by a comprehensive presentation to a meeting of PICAO hosted jointly by TRE and TFU at Malvern and Defford, in September 1946. The highlight of the meeting was the demonstration to international delegates of auto-homing, orbiting, approach and landing in the Boeing.[134] The meeting was spread over three weeks, with three days in each week devoted to flying demonstrations. For this purpose, the 100 or so delegates were

Another photo by Vern Manion, showing the Boeing engineer Fred Baker with RAF ground engineers. Note the 'blind landing' designation triangle on the side of the nose of the Boeing 247-D. The hatch over the pilots' cockpit is open. (The Boeing Company)

divided into parties of eight. A flight in the Boeing was scheduled for each party, with a demonstration of automatic landing and what was now referred to as 'RADORA' (radar orbit and approach). The PICAO meeting and demonstrations were deemed so successful that the Ministry of Supply and the Ministry of Civil Aviation jointly decided to offer the facilities at Malvern and Defford to the Air Ministry for further displays.[135] These took place on 30th September, 1st and 2nd October 1946, attended by 130 RAF and Dominion air forces personnel, including Air Marshal Sir Norman Bottomley of Bomber Command, six Air Vice-Marshals and seven Air Commodores, representing all the flying Commands of the RAF.

In preparation for the PICAO meeting in September, and in anticipation of further trials to come, in August 1946 the Boeing was allocated specifically to 'auto homing and orbiting (for) PICAO'. A pilot new to the Boeing, Flt Lt Eric Knowles DFM, was given responsibility for much of the flying involved. In the course of the demonstrations to PICAO and the Air Ministry, he flew with delegates as passengers on no less than 22 occasions, between 11th September and 2nd October 1946. With other pilots, including McDonald himself, also being involved in the flying, this shows the intensity of use which was being made of the old Boeing in this period.

Eric Knowles was a very experienced pilot who had gained his Private Pilot's Licence back in November 1938, and had joined TFU at Defford in November 1944 after a distinguished record with Coastal Command, including the sinking of the German submarine U-541. His first flight on the Boeing was on 13th May 1946, as second pilot to Flt Lt Ellis. He did not fly the Boeing again until 30th August, but after that date he flew it very regularly on trials and demonstration work, including 14 flights during the PICAO meeting. In total, he logged 18 hours on 31 flights over eight weeks culminating in the latter part of October.

However, the writing was now on the wall for DZ203. The demonstrations for PICAO proved to be the old airliner's swan song. In the returns of aircraft involved in research and development work at TFU, for the week ending 18th October, the Boeing was no longer featured under the heading 'Aircraft Employed' but was now listed under the heading 'Aircraft Up for Disposal'. This followed a round trip to Martlesham Heath by Gp Capt McDonald, accompanied by a Sqn Ldr Scott, on 10th October. McDonald had his last flight in the Boeing on 18th October, piloting an auto-landing demonstration to Sqn Ldr Samuelson, with Fg Off Barber as crew. Flt Lt Knowles flew to Martlesham Heath on 21st October, with one other person on board, returning the same day with three passengers. This may have been the last flight of Boeing 247-D DZ203. Soon after, Eric Knowles gave up flying duties, switching to ground duties as an Air Traffic Controller at Defford in February 1947.

On 11th November 1946, Gp Capt McDonald (now CBE AFC) took retirement from the RAF and left Defford, to become the first Commandant of the new transatlantic airport at Prestwick.

In this group photo taken at Defford in 1948, in the front row, extreme left, is Flt Lt Eric Knowles, who regularly piloted the Boeing on automatic landing demonstrations and trials in 1946. The three officers in the middle of the front row are Wg Cdr C. Southwell, Gp Capt D.R. Evans (Station Commander, Defford) and Lt Cdr Hudson RN (OC Royal Navy Section). The first three named of these four, all piloted Boeing 247-D DZ203 at various times, while earlier the Royal Navy section and Lt Cdr Hudson's predecessor, had been involved closely in the 3 cm radar trials. (Roger Knowles)

With exquisite timing, the two veterans – John McDonald and his Boeing – retired from flying service with the RAF within a few days of each other.

McDonald was succeeded as Station Commander at Defford by Gp Capt D R Evans CBE DFC – the very same Donald Randell Evans, who as a Wing Commander and CO of the FIU, had flown the Boeing on 10 cm AI radar trials at Ford in August 1941. Whether he remembered the Boeing, and whether he went to pay his last respects to the old airliner after his arrival at Defford, we will never know.

10. BLEU AND THE DEMISE OF THE BOEING

Wg Cdr Frank Griffiths was posted in September 1945 to be CO of the RAF contingent at the new Blind Landing Experimental Unit (BLEU). To explain the origins of this unit, and the ultimate effect this had on the Boeing, it is necessary to go back to late 1943, when the requirement for the project on automatic landing was formulated.

In view of the outstanding success of the Boeing with automatic landing, in retrospect it is difficult to imagine how this could have been achieved other than by trials at Defford under the direction of the radar scientists of TRE at Malvern. Yet it could have been very different, as automatic landing was the subject of a serious and at times acrimonious interdepartmental demarcation dispute. Elements at RAE Farnborough regarded automatic landing as their territory. Farnborough had been the home of Government sponsored experimental aviation in Britain since the earliest days of flying. It appears some of the civil service scientists at RAE did not take kindly to the wartime upstarts at TRE, mostly university people seconded for the duration of the war, and the service aircrew and technicians at Defford, with their reputation for disregard of protocol and total focus on getting the job done.

TRE at Malvern and at Defford reported to the Ministry of Aircraft Production (MAP), whose broad responsibility was to ensure the air forces received the aircraft and equipment they needed. TFU, the flying side at Defford, reported to 10 Group, RAF.

The need for a totally reliable all-weather landing system, and the application of radar technologies to achieve automatic landing, was recognised by late 1943. MAP sought to decide where responsibilities lay between different research establishments by setting up an Automatic Blind Landing Technical Advisory Panel (ABLTAP) at the start of 1944. But RAE at Farnborough objected to TRE representation on this panel. In response, Air Cdre Leedham of MAP wrote to W G A Perring of RAE on 26th February 1944. He explained the need to make fullest use of TRE experience, the intention being that a full appreciation of available radar and radio systems would be carried out by TRE, taking into account post-war civil applications as well, after which the experimental work would be carried out at RAE. Perring was not impressed. He wrote: *'TRE should not have more than one representative on the Panel ... Radio Dept. at RAE are the real authorities on SBA and Glide Path'.* While work on the Boeing proceeded at Defford, discontent at RAE rumbled on.

On the 19th June 1944, Sir Robert Renwick chaired a meeting at which it was ruled Glide Path should have a high priority at TRE, stating TRE must work on the addition of a Glide Path system to Lucero[136] airborne beacon interrogator system *'...ultimately for the application of this information directly to the autopilot for automatic approach and landing',* A complete SCS-51 system on order from the United States would be directed to TRE. This work was to have A* priority, followed by a radar glide path under development at TRE, priority A.

This was all recorded in a memo from MAP to TRE on 22nd July 1944, and copied to the WT (Radio) Department at RAE . This document survives in the National Archives at Kew.[137] Scribbled across the top of the memo is written: *'This cuts right across our responsibility for automatic blind landing. Who was present at this meeting on June 19th, and were we represented? It is clearly not for DCD to instruct the co-ordinator where the work is to be undertaken. Please let me have your comments as soon as possible'.* People at RAE were clearly unhappy, and apparently unaware that RAE and TRE were working under the Director Technical Development (DTD) and Director Communications Development (DCD) respectively, who worked closely together and were in complete agreement at MAP headquarters - the two were acting jointly in response to the top priority Air Staff Requirement for the development of a fully automatic system for blind landing.

While rapid progress was being made at Defford, discontent in the Radio Department at RAE continued. An outspoken four-page memo from M Birchall at RAE, dated 30th December 1944, argued for a greater part for RAE and its Radio Department in automatic landing. But he remarked bitterly, *'... RAE haven't got SCS-51 or a Honeywell*

Flight Engineer Rex Allison in the cockpit of DZ203 in May 1946. This photo was by George Stalker, a flight engineer at Defford, who had previously completed a tour as an air gunner with Bomber Command, and later re-mustered as a pilot, flying Canberras and V-bombers. (The late George Stalker)

autopilot. We should make it clear the proper home for this job is RAE'. He complained that the work of RAE to provide coupling from BABS to a Mk VIII Auto Pilot was being held up, even though he admitted the Mk VIII was unsuitable for this purpose. Meanwhile he said: *'TRE are taking the American line and putting in a lot of high-grade people and effort into the project. Griffiths is employed solely on this type of work and regarded by all as the eminent authority on American systems. We should claim this work and the equipment that goes with it. There is a proposal to set up a special unit – RAE should try to secure a controlling interest in this'.*

For his part, Frank Griffiths wrote many years later: *'Hell hath nothing to compare with the jealousy of one scientific establishment for another where research is concerned'.*

Group Captain Frank Griffiths, DFC, AFC, Legion d'Honneur, Croix de Guerre, Flying Cross (Netherlands), who was the first to pilot the Boeing in Britain in August 1941, and as Officer Commanding Flying at Defford, flew many of the automatic landing trials in DZ203 in 1945. (Lloyd Cromwell Griffiths)

In fact, as Air Cdre Leedham had made clear at the outset, once the various elements and options for their use had been proven at Defford under DCD, the experimental work would transfer to the aegis of Farnborough and DTD, as had been intended all along. With the end of the war in Europe and the rapid rundown of numbers at TRE and TFU, and the effective completion of the trials programme for the Boeing on automatic homing, orbit and landing, this duly happened.

The acrimony and bitterness mainly seems to have emanated from the Radio Department at RAE. Others at Farnborough, in particular the Instrument Department and the Aerodynamics Department, took a more constructive and co-operative approach, both readily accepting that the radio and radar work required was well within the capabilities of TRE and TFU. But they also appreciated that for the whole project to succeed, more would be needed from these two RAE departments in their own respective fields. The full implications of coupling radio outputs to the autopilot needed to be explored, and this was seen as a job for the Instrument Department at RAE. While the Boeing, with its shallow glide angle and low stalling speed was ideal for initial trials, the system needed to be applied to other types of aircraft in general use, and with an eye to future types, so some involvement of the Aerodynamics Department at RAE would also be needed. Work started at Farnborough on these aspects and ran in parallel with the flight trials being carried out at Defford throughout the rest of 1944 and into 1945, with the mechanical differential analyser at Manchester University being used to investigate the stability and flight path performance of an aircraft on automatic approach.

With close collaboration evident between TRE and the Instrument and Aerodynamics Departments at RAE, the co-ordinating Advisory Panel decided in June 1945 that the time had come with the end of the

Boeing 247-D DZ203 at Defford in 1946, showing the overall 'silver' (aluminium) finish adopted after the war. (The Boeing Company)

War in Europe, to form a new unit amalgamating the TRE and RAE teams as the Blind Landing Experimental Unit (BLEU). This was to be an outstation of RAE, based at Martlesham Heath in Suffolk, although initially operating from the vast runway at nearby RAF Woodbridge.

BLEU was formed under the direction of Mr H C Pritchard, reporting to Dr G W H Gardner, the Head of the Instrument Department at Farnborough – the man whom Griffiths was so anxious to impress with the demonstration of the Boeing in April 1945. RAF and scientific staff started assembling at Woodbridge during the summer of 1945, and flying got under way in September. Frank Griffiths was posted from RAF Defford (with a pilot rating of 'Exceptional') on 24th September, to be the first RAF Commanding Officer of BLEU. The scientific staff who came from Farnborough quickly discovered that Griffiths, a man of many talents, was not only an enthusiastic sailor in small boats, but also a budding smallholder. He made his arrival at Woodbridge on 27th September, flying from Defford in a Lancaster. When the doors of the aircraft were opened, the first things to emerge were a collection of chickens in their coops.[138] His log book shows that on board the Lancaster that day, he had eleven passengers - it is not known if this figure included the chickens.

It does not appear that much use was made of the Boeing at Woodbridge, although Griffiths flew regularly to and fro between Woodbridge and Defford. He was at Defford on 31st October 1945 in the Boeing, when he flew a demonstration with 'various bods' on board, and again on 6th November with '3 C.A. personnel', also at Defford. The only visits of the Boeing to BLEU of which records survive, were late in the life of the old airliner, in the autumn of 1946, when McDonald flew in on 10th October, and then the flight by Eric Knowles on 21st October.

The visit of Gp Capt McDonald to Martlesham Heath on 10th October 1946 may well have been to decide whether BLEU had any use for the Boeing, and the answer, based on the later recollections of Frank Griffiths, was evidently 'no'.

By this date Griffiths had left BLEU, being posted on 5th February 1946, to Canada, where he attended the RCAF Staff College at Armour Heights, Toronto. On his return to Britain, he joined Transport Command as a Staff Officer with No. 47 Group, and was involved in checking the routes flown by Transport Command for the Middle and Far East Air Forces. In November 1946, he was in Ceylon, but returned to Britain the following month. While with HQ 47 Group at Milton Ernest Hall in Bedfordshire, he flew out of Little Staughton, where he had the use of Miles Messenger RG327 as a runabout. He made day visits to Defford on 17th December 1946, and on 7th May 1947, on both occasions in the Messenger.

So with Griffiths being mostly far away from Defford, his memory of what happened next to the Boeing must have been based on what he was told after the event. He wrote: *'Although the Boeing 247-D had been the means of bringing us as a nation into the forefront of Auto-landing, it was finally handed back to TRE at Defford. This may have been pique on the part of our new masters, RAE Farnborough, who maybe did not like this evidence of another establishment's accomplishment. But this Boeing, RAF No. DZ203, proved to me that aeroplanes have souls. We had flown together on and off for nearly five years, and she went back to Defford, in my opinion heartbroken. She was parked in a hangar which during the war had been erected for camouflage purposes close to oak trees. One night a mighty Worcestershire oak blew down, smashed through the hangar roof and broke the Boeing's back. That was the end of the Boeing'.*

Contrary to Griffiths' wonderfully romantic account, the truth was almost certainly more prosaic. When the Boeing was rebuilt in 1944, the objective was to give it another 200 flying hours. In 1945, it had, by Gp Capt McDonald's account, flown over 300 hours on automatic landing trials and demonstrations alone. By the autumn of 1946, it was in need of another major overhaul. At a meeting on 3rd October, called with a view to reducing the number of aircraft held at Defford, and chaired by McDonald, it was decided that the Boeing should be released, but no date was set for this. It was accepted that the benign flying characteristics and shallow glide angle of the Boeing were far from typical of contemporary military and civil types, so neither

Defford nor BLEU saw any further use for it, and inevitably, it was put up for disposal. John McDonald had planned to fly the Boeing to Farnborough on 24th October, but this trip was cancelled, marking the end of the road for DZ203.

The demonstrations and trials for PICAO had indeed proved to be the old airliner's swan song. On 30th October 1946, a meeting of the Aircraft Establishment Committee[139] at Defford, confirmed the reduction in number of aircraft to be based there, from 16 four-engine, 40 twin-engine and 11 single-engine aircraft, to 10, 20 and 10 respectively, which took into account the disposal of the Boeing.

In the weekly return for 22nd November, the status of the Boeing changes from 'Up for disposal' to 'Awaiting scrapping', and appears as such every week until 12th December, after which there is no further mention of the Boeing in the returns at Defford.

The Air Ministry 'Aircraft Movement' card (Form 78) records that Boeing 247-D DZ203 was 'Struck off Charge' on 26th December 1946. Being Boxing Day and so a public holiday, this date might seem a bit unlikely, especially in the more leisurely atmosphere of the post-war RAF. The Defford ORB records that from 23rd to 29th December 1946, the Station was closed, except for key personnel, 'for the Christmas Grant'. Phil Butler suggests a possible reason for this date of entry might be that the necessary form (F149) to effect the procedure for striking the aircraft off charge was written on 26th December by one of the 'key personnel' not on leave and trying to pass the time. Alternatively the form was dealt with on that day by some unfortunate on duty over Boxing Day in the relevant Air Ministry 'Stats' Office.

There are varying accounts of the circumstances of gale damage that led to the Boeing's demise at Defford, apart from Frank Griffiths account.

Peter Berry, having been trained as a Flight Mechanic, was posted to Defford in early 1946, and assigned to the 'Duty Crew' section. In his unpublished memoirs[140] and in a more recent article[141], he records that at this time those associated with the automatic landing trials had left for Martlesham Heath, although the Boeing was still at Defford. Later in the year, he was sent on a 14-week course to RAF Locking. On his return, he was assigned to the Servicing Wing, and '... *by this time the Boeing 247-D had been damaged in a storm when a Worcester oak tree blew down across the hangar in which it was stored*'. The wording suggests he may have drawn on that used by Griffiths in his book 'Angel Visits'. However, it is clear from Peter Berry's account that there was gale damage to the Boeing while stored in a hangar, and this took place while he was away at Locking.

In January and February 1947, Britain suffered abnormally low temperatures and excessively heavy snowfall. The severe weather continued into March with even greater ferocity, as temperatures dropped to below -20°C in places. From 1st to 7th March 1947, Defford suffered the heaviest snowfall yet, with the camp almost cut off, and a Sikorsky Hoverfly helicopter offering the only form of transport in and out. On 5th March, a blizzard with easterly gales was described as 'the worst storm in these parts ever recorded'[142], and on 15th March, an even worse gale hit the airfield, with wind speeds averaging 40mph and gusting up to 70mph, causing £700 of damage. The subsequent thaw was to create devastating problems of its own, with aircraft from Defford being pressed into service to drop inflatable bomber dinghies to stranded farms in the flooded Severn valley.

This might be taken to suggest the damage to the Boeing took place on 6th March or 16th March 1947, as the Defford ORB does not mention gale damage on any other date during that winter. However, it was also very cold in Worcestershire with strong easterly winds in December 1946 and January 1947, with hurricane-force winds recorded in Birmingham (40 miles away) in mid-January. So although the gales of 6th and 16th March and the damage caused merited a mention in the ORB, perhaps damage to an aircraft that had already been Struck Off Charge was not seen as worth recording. Peter Berry knows he was back from his course at Locking and at Defford on 24th February, by which time the gale damage to the Boeing had taken place. Taking together Berry's memory of events and the weekly

This photo by Vern Manion, evidently taken by the Boeing photographer at Defford in 1946, was published in the Boeing Magazine for February 1947. It appears to show DZ203 in the process of having silver paint applied to remove the outer yellow of the roundel – in the course of doing so, the last digit of the serial number has been painted over. (The Boeing Company)

returns, these suggest the gale damage to the Boeing could have occurred any time between 12th December 1946 (after which date it was no longer recorded even as 'awaiting scrapping'), and 24th February 1947.

There is another contemporary account, from the late George Stalker, who was stationed at Defford at this time, having been posted to ground duties after serving as an air gunner with Bomber Command. He subsequently re-mustered as a flight engineer, before being selected for pilot training. After postings to Canberra and V-bomber squadrons, he completed his final flying tour at the Royal Radar Establishment (RRE) Pershore in the late 1960s. He was proud to have worn three different brevets - possibly a unique achievement in the Royal Air Force? In his account, Stalker concurs that gale damage was the cause of the final demise of the Boeing, but states this was a consequence of the aircraft being blown backwards out of the open-ended blister hangar in which it was stored.[143] He does not mention a particular date, only that this happened in the severe winter of 1947.

It seems reasonable to suppose that after the decision had been taken to scrap the Boeing, the aircraft was kept in a hangar (with the run-down of the establishment there would no shortage of storage space), with a view to a leisurely process of stripping out the experimental equipment. The MAP Form 2101 record card for DZ203 is silent about this period, there being nothing on the card between the entry dated 19th December 1945 *Retention approved for use as a Flying Laboratory'* and the final entry, which reads as follows:

'Date 12.8.47. Allotted to 34 MU. From Defford, Cat E2 Scrap., ref. 43G/936/DZ203, delivered 9/7/47, Allotment RD/D 4090; Engines to 327764/- 327627/- To No. 2 MPRD Cat E2 ref. 430/936/DZ203, 9/7/47, Allotment RD/F2621'.

On 9th July 1947, the mortal remains of the Boeing were delivered to 34 MU as Category E2 (defined as 'aircraft struck off charge and only suitable for scrap'). 34 MU was at Montford Bridge near Shrewsbury, although it was shortly to move to nearby Sleap airfield.[144] The ORB of 34 MU at Montford Bridge shows that in the month of July 1947, this unit received 50 aircraft, of which 28 were category E1 and E2 scrap, arriving by road and rail.[145] The Unit Main Party moved to Sleap on 14th July, but a Rear Party of one officer and 18 airmen remained behind at Montford Bridge to continue sending equipment over to Sleap, the final 'marching out inspection' at Montford Bridge being at the end of July.

While the entry in MAP Form 2101 for DZ203 would seem beyond dispute, over the years the fate of the Boeing seems to have become something of an intriguing mystery to those fascinated by this unique aircraft, with various conflicting accounts published. Some sources suggest DZ203 was still flying in 1948[146], which clearly cannot be so. A review of American aircraft in the British services 1914 – 1955, published in 1957, reported that the Boeing had been returned to the United States[147], but again more recent research confirms this was not the case. Peter Berry stated in an article published in 1997[148], that the Boeing was broken up by Cunliffe-Owen Aircraft at Southampton. This may have been based on the comment in the Air Britain 'Impressments Log' by Peter Moss, published in 1962, that the *'Last known details of the Boeing, are derived from photographs which portray the 247-D having its R.A.F. markings painted over by R.A.F. personnel. Judging from the negative numbers of the photos the Boeing was at Cunliffe-Owen's airfield'.* However, the photograph in the 'Impressments Log' of the Boeing being repainted appears identical to one in the series taken by the Boeing photographer at Defford in 1946. So the suggestion of Cunliffe-Owen being involved at this stage is almost certainly misleading, and Cunliffe-Owen (who were located at Eastleigh) did not carry out the scrapping of DZ203.

It can be concluded that there is little or no doubt that the Boeing was scrapped at 34 MU. But as 34 MU moved from Montford Bridge to Sleap in July 1947, one cannot be certain whether DZ203 was broken up for scrap at Montford Bridge, or at Sleap.

A former airman with 34 MU, Bill Mathias, who was in the Mechanised Transport (MT) section, recalls the Boeing 247-D arriving at Montford Bridge. Bill Mathias died in 2010, but he provided Mike Grant of the Wartime Aircraft Recovery Group with useful information on aircraft types scrapped at 34 MU. Mike Grant told the author that Bill Mathias was clear in his recollection – it was a twin-engine Boeing, not a B-17, and it had been used for radar research, although the interior had been stripped of all equipment before it arrived at Montford Bridge.

However, by 9th July, the date the Boeing was delivered to 34 MU, the move of personnel and equipment from Montford Bridge to Sleap was already in progress, in particular the heavy power saws that were used to chop aircraft into pieces which would fit in a railway truck or road vehicle. So although it is possible DZ203 was broken up shortly after arriving at Montford Bridge, it may well have been moved on to Sleap to be cut up and consigned to scrap. Metallic scrap from 34 MU was sent to No. 2 Metal Produce Recovery Depot (MPRD) at

Eaglescliffe in County Durham. In August 1947, 34 MU despatched 75 tons by road and 48 tons by rail.

If the Boeing arrived at Montford Bridge but was then transferred to Sleap for scrapping that could explain the time interval between the delivery from Defford on 7th July, and 12th August 1947, the date of the final entry on the MAP Form 2101.

ABOVE—Before wearing the RAF insignia, the 247-D flew for United and Inland Air Lines and the Canadian Air Force. RIGHT—The plane was flying out of Defford when it passed its 10,000th hour. Crew commemorated event with plaque.

BOEING DZ 203 1947

BOEING DZ 203
Constructed SEATTLE U.S.A.
27th JULY 1933.

On 14th April 1944
this AIRCRAFT flew
its TEN THOUSANDTH HOUR

Whilst en-route
BARROW—DEFFORD.

KING-SIZE JOB

"Old No. 1726" was one of the world's most advanced-type transports when it left the factory in the summer of 1933. As a member of the Boeing 247 family, it was to play a leading role in the development of modern air transportation. Going on fourteen now, the elderly plane is still up to its wing-tips in development work.

Despite its age and its number of flying hours — almost 12,000 — the plane was specially selected by England's Royal Air Force for testing of modern radio, radar, electronics and navigational aids. Mod-

ified, but still a Boeing, the 247-D is stationed at Defford, Worcestershire, in the RAF's Telecommunications Flying Unit. Experiments involve the study of remotely-controlled take-offs and landing with auto pilots, blind landing beams and other high-frequency radio installations.

According to British flyers working with the Boeing, the ship was selected for this work because of its ruggedness, reliability, ease of maintenance and excellent stability characteristics.

Fred Baker (left), Boeing service engineer who ran across "Old 1726" at Defford, inspects new power plant RAF installed. Engines develop 600 hp; old ones had 550 hp rating.

The 247, whose type was forerunner of modern commercial transports, now carries electronic equipment. RAF feels plane is well suited for job and good for many more hours.

A page from the Boeing Magazine *for February 1947, with Vern Manion's story and photographs of the visit to Defford of Boeing Engineer Fred Baker to see* 'Old 1726' — *the Boeing 247-D DZ203.* (Courtesy Michael J Lombardi, The Boeing Company)

APPENDIX A – HOW MANY HOURS DID THE BOEING FLY?

Conflicting figures have been published for the final recorded airframe flying hours for Boeing 247-D DZ203, with estimates ranging up to 14,000 hours, a figure provided by George Stalker[149] who was present at Defford in 1946.

On 9th August 1940, the day before the purchase of the Boeing by Charles H Babb on behalf of the Canadian Government, 'Total Aircraft Flying Time' was recorded on the CAA Aircraft Inspection Report as 9,766 hours. As flying hours were recorded in the FAA file regularly as they mounted from 1933 onwards, this figure can be verified. In airline service, which of course represented a totally different situation to its later use as a research aircraft, the Boeing as NC13344 averaged around 1,400 hours per year.

When the Boeing moved to Canada, the delivery flight from Wyoming to Trenton might have accounted for 12 hours; nothing is known of hours flown at Trenton, but Terry Judge suggests an estimated figure of 30 hours. The flight log of the Test and Development Flight (TDF) at Rockcliffe shows just over 2 hours for the Boeing till the end of March. The transfer flight from Rockcliffe to Boston would account for perhaps 3 hours. It is stated in contemporary correspondence that the Boeing, after installation of 10 cm AI radar, and the flight from Canada to the United States, flew 40 hours over a ten-week period at Boston, April-June 1941, before being shipped to England.[150] All this suggests the aircraft flew around 100 hours in Canada and at Boston, so must have completed at least 9,860 hours by the time it arrived in Britain.

This makes it difficult to accept the statement on the plaque in the cabin of DZ203, recording that the aircraft reached the total of 10,000 flying hours on 14th April 1944, shortly before the Boeing became subject to an extensive refurbishment, including fitting new engines. This figure of 10,000 hours for the Boeing, as at April 1944, is also quoted in TFU Report No. 70, so clearly was generally accepted as correct at Defford. If true, however, this would suggest that the aircraft flew no more than 140 hours, in nearly four years with the TFU before its rebuild in 1944. In the light of the known fairly intensive use of the Boeing during much of this period, it seems a very low figure, even bearing in mind the pattern of intermittent short flights to which it may have been subjected as a research aircraft.

From surviving documents, such as minutes of monthly progress meetings at Defford, it is not possible to add up the total hours flown by the Boeing, as flying hours are recorded by project ('Item'), not by individual aircraft, and so take no account of hours flown by an aircraft in any one month when not devoted to a specific project. However, if we take hours flown on one project, Item 45 'AIX Tests', in four months July - October 1942 when only the Boeing was involved and during which time we can be fairly sure this aircraft was not involved in anything else, this totals 60 hours or an average of 15 hours per month. That rate of utilisation over the 32 months from August 1941, would add up to 480 hours, and bring the total to around 10,330 hours by April 1944. This of course does not include flying hours when the Boeing was not on experimental work, but being used for other duties such as passenger carrying, and ferrying pilots and equipment. In view of the longer duration of some of these tasks, and the popularity of the Boeing for this purpose, this type of flying could have made a substantial contribution to the aircraft's total flying hours.

Adding up the number of flying hours recorded in the surviving log books of pilots who flew the Boeing between August 1941 and April 1944, the total from these few flights alone comes to around 90 hours, while these can only represent a small fraction of the total flying time of the aircraft during that period. As a conservative estimate, it seems more likely that the flying time of the Boeing was around 10,500 hours in mid-1944 when it was rebuilt, and if so, the figure on the plaque for April 1944 was wrong.

There may be a clue to the eventual true figure, in that at a meeting in October 1942, Frank Griffiths as CO of 'B' Flight (Offensive Section)

Commemorative plaque attached to the door in the centre of the rear cabin bulkhead of DZ203, which reads: 'BOEING DZ203. Constructed Seattle USA 27th July 1933. On 14th April 1944, this AIRCRAFT flew its TEN THOUSANDTH HOUR whilst en route BARROW-DEFFORD'. *This photo by Vern Manion, was published in the corporate Boeing Magazine for February 1947, but only after being retouched to remove the light reflection and, perhaps to make the story more topical, the date above the plaque changed to 1947!* (The Boeing Company)

where the Boeing was allotted, was asked what he considered to be the Boeing's remaining useful flying life, in view of the absence of spares for this aircraft. Griffiths replied the aircraft was in very good condition, with at least another 170 hours expected. The UAL manual specifies an engine change, replacing the engines with overhauled units, at not more than 695 hours. If this was the figure Griffiths had in mind, then that would suggest that he understood the Boeing had flown around 500 hours since last overhauled at Cheyenne, this would of course take the total hours to well over 10,000 at this date.

John McDonald stated that after re-building, the Boeing flew over 300 hours on trials and demonstrations in the year 1945, to which could be added perhaps a further 200 hours in 1946.

All this suggests a total over life of at least 11,000 hours, and perhaps even the 'almost 12,000 hours' estimated for the benefit of the Boeing photographer who visited Defford in 1946, but some way short of the figure of 14,000 hours quoted by George Stalker.

APPENDIX B – WHAT DID THE BOEING IN BRITAIN LOOK LIKE?

When the Boeing 247-D reached Britain in 1941, the ground 'walk-round' and the air-to-air photos, taken soon after arrival, showed there were few external indications of its experimental role, apart from the bulge under the new moulded plywood nose. Otherwise, the external profile of the nose remained similar to that of an unmodified 247-D airliner.

It is not known when the Boeing was camouflaged with RAF markings, but this was probably done before leaving North America, as the demarcation line on the fuselage between the Dark Green and Dark Earth upper surfaces and the yellow under surface, formed a wavy line, which is characteristic of what seemed to be the American interpretation of RAF camouflage at this time. However, the painter must have had a shaky hand when he did the starboard rear fuselage as the wavy line was distinctly irregular! The upper surfaces were painted in standard camouflage pattern No.2, promulgated in 1941 for twin-engine monoplanes not exceeding 70 feet wing span, in the temperate land scheme. The yellow under surface was as prescribed for trainers, transport, communication and miscellaneous aircraft. The national identity markings were as specified by Air Ministry instructions; these were defined by the late Bruce Robertson[151] as A1 roundel (outer ring yellow) on the fuselage and B type (blue and red only) over-wing. Under-wing roundels were red, white and blue, type A(i) (with no yellow outer), and there was a rectangular red, white and blue fin flash. The photograph taken before the Boeing left Canada shows the aircraft in a plain finish with its Canadian serial 7655, and British-style roundels typical of RCAF aircraft – another Canadian 247-D, serial number 7635, shows the roundels to be type A(i) above and below the wings, A1 on fuselage sides, with the fin flash covering each side of the fin. The plain finish of the Canadian 247s may in fact have been unpainted, with a matt grey (and sometimes patchy) appearance resulting from an anodic treatment of all external duralumin surfaces. This appearance remained with most 247s and 247-Ds until 1940, when United's aircraft were painted white, and it seems likely that those which went to Canada missed this treatment. A letter to Air Pictorial in 1962[152] on the subject of the Canadian 247-Ds asked in passing, *'Why were these* (Boeings) *always painted grey?'* The answer would appear to be that they were not painted at all! The Canadian photograph of 7655 shows propellers with four or five rows of contrasting bands which extend from the tips well down the blades. This safety feature was seen on many UAL and ex-United Boeings. By the time it arrived at Christchurch as DZ203 however, the Boeing had only the tips painted in a light colour, presumably yellow.

The air-to-air photographs, even though taken soon after the freshly-painted Boeing arrived in Britain, appear to show considerable scuff marks on the top of the fuselage, and on the fin. Also evident is a notice pasted on the inside of the window in the main cabin access door, which is on the starboard side. As mentioned earlier, the fact that a window was fitted in this door is unusual for a Boeing 247-D. On the port side was the door to the luggage compartment, which was aft of the cabin. There was also an emergency escape for passengers via the fifth and rearmost window on the port side. In American airline service there would have been a toilet, aft of cabin on the starboard side, with a skylight in the roof of the fuselage over[153], but the skylight is no longer visible in the 1941 photographs of the Boeing.

At some point, perhaps in late 1941, the moulded 'wooden' nose may have been replaced with a moulded 'Perspex' one, but it apparently reverted to moulded plywood before 1945. By then there was no longer a bulge visible under the nose. This nose was damaged by the nose-over landing in April 1945, and the consequent emergency patching, with thin strips of plywood moulded and glued on, remained evident in 1946 and can be seen in photographs taken at that time. Although painted Perspex radomes had become commonplace, McDonald says the nose compartment of the Boeing was 'wooden' at this time.[154] Griffiths describes the nose of the Boeing during the automatic landing trials as being made of 'plastic' but this is not necessarily inconsistent with it actually being a moulded resin/plywood composite. Certainly, the fact that the nose was not shattered by the nose-over, and was repaired with comparative ease with strips of plywood does suggest that, whether or not the Boeing was fitted with a Perspex nose during the mid-war years, by 1945 it had a moulded plywood one.

In 1942, the British national markings on the Boeing were changed to roundels and fin flash where the white and (where relevant) yellow bands were much narrower – the type C markings. In 1944, a yellow triangle was painted on each side of the nose – this was the approved symbol for aircraft being used for Beam Approach Training, so seemed appropriate for an aircraft which was being used for 'Blind Landing' trials.

When the Boeing was rebuilt at Defford in 1944, this resulted in significant changes to its appearance. The S1H1-G Wasp engines, with long-chord NACA cowlings, were replaced by R-1340-AN-1 Wasps, with the shorter chord cowlings typical of the Harvard. This left more of the tapered nacelle behind the engine exposed, giving a somewhat ungainly appearance. The three-bladed propellers were replaced by the two-bladed type as fitted to the Harvard.

At some time, probably in early 1946, the Boeing was repainted in 'silver' (aluminium) finish overall, the new post-war scheme for transport aircraft. It appears that initially, although the aircraft was finished silver, the roundels were still the C type with yellow outer rings. A photo taken in 1946, shows an RAF airman apparently painting over the yellow outer rings with aluminium paint, in the course of which he has painted over the '3' of the serial DZ203. The effect of removing the yellow outer ring would be to display the prescribed C1 roundels on the fuselage and C type roundels on the upper surface of the wings, with no yellow surrounds. The yellow triangles on either side of the nose remained. There are no photographs showing the underside of the Boeing at this stage in its career, but it was an early post-war requirement for all RAF aircraft that the serial number, in black on aluminium painted aircraft, should be displayed on the underside of each wing.

APPENDIX C – WHAT REMAINS?

The pattern of the runways and some buildings can still be seen from the air at Montford Bridge airfield, where the airframe of Boeing DZ203, was delivered to 34 MU for scrapping in July 1947. But it is unlikely any fragments of the Boeing will be found at Montford Bridge if, as seems quite possible, the aircraft was transferred to Sleap for breaking up. At Sleap, it can be assumed that as scrap metal was in considerable demand in post-war Britain, 34 MU would have acted fairly promptly in sending the pieces of the broken-up airframe to Eaglescliffe. It is just possible that some discarded relics of the Boeing found their way to the airfield dump at Sleap. This was in a quarry, 120 feet deep and quarter of a mile across, just outside the northern boundary of the airfield. However, the quarry was subsequently used as a landfill site by the local authority. So if there are any relics from 34 MU of aviation interest in the former quarry at Sleap, they are a long way down, buried under countless tons of domestic waste - a daunting prospect for even the most enthusiastic aviation archaeologist! But it is possible some relics from the Boeing may yet be found at Defford, where the aircraft was maintained, modified, repaired, and ultimately stripped for scrapping. Searches by the archaeologists of the Defford Airfield Heritage Group for aviation relics on the former airfield continue. Recent discoveries have included an intact radome, which in size, shape and fittings, matches that fitted to Barracuda DP855/G to house a scanner for ASVX radar, which was a direct outcome of the pioneering work carried out by Boeing 247-D DZ203/G.

There is an intact Boeing 247-D in Britain, in the keeping of the Science Museum, at its aircraft store at Wroughton airfield in Wiltshire. This facility is not normally open to the public, but the aircraft may be seen by prior arrangement. This aircraft is c/n 1722, which was from the same batch as DZ203, and as NC13340 it similarly served with NAT, UAL and PCA up to 1940. It became NC18, serving with the Civil Aeronautics Administration (CAA) of the US Department of Commerce, and after the war flew as N18E with various small airlines and private owners. In 1982, N18E, now somewhat underpowered with R-985 Wasp Junior engines, and not having flown for three years, made an epic flight across the Atlantic to join the Science Museum in Britain.

There are at least three other preserved Boeings. A 247-D that was another of those sold to Canada, and which served with the RCAF as 7638, is in the Canada Aviation and Space Museum in Ottawa. The 1934 'MacRobertson' Race commercial section runner-up flown by Roscoe Turner, later NC13369 with UAL, is in the National Air and Space Museum of the Smithsonian Institution in Washington, DC. Like the Boeing now at Wroughton, this 247-D served with the CAA of the US Dept. of Commerce during and after the Second World War, on experimental work that included automatic landing trials. Perhaps the best known surviving 247-D is 'City of Renton', c/n 1729, NC13347, now with The Museum of Flight in Seattle and probably the last 247 to be airworthy. As with the Boeing that came to Britain, 'City of Renton' had served with UAL, PCA, and the RCAF.

Defford airfield was closed to flying in late 1957, but most of the 18th century landscaped grounds of Croome Park, on which part of Defford airfield was built in 1941, are now in the hands of the National Trust and like Croome Court itself, are open to the public. The National Trust has preserved and restored several of the former RAF buildings, which contain displays on the life and activities of Defford airfield and the vital part played by the Telecommunications Flying Unit in the development of airborne radar. TRE was amalgamated with the Radar Research and Development Establishment (RRDE, also located in Malvern) in 1953, to form the Radar Research Establishment (RRE), although the TFU was not renamed the Radar Research Flying Unit (RRFU) until 1955. However, the main runway at Defford was too short for the large jet bombers then entering service, so it was decided to move the RRFU to nearby Pershore airfield, and most of its aircraft left Defford in September 1957.

Whilst most of the airfield's buildings and ground structures were then demolished, the runway structure remained in the hands of RRE, which became the Royal Radar Establishment in 1957.

A surviving Boeing 247-D, formerly NC13340, now preserved by the Science Museum at Wroughton. This was a sister ship to NC13344, and similarly served with NAT, UAL and PCA up to 1940. (Author's photograph, by permission of the Science Museum)

Between 1958 and 1960, a large radio telescope facility was built on Defford airfield. It comprised two 85ft diameter steerable dishes mounted on trolleys which could be moved along railway tracks laid along two of the runways. The facility was used in defence research applications by the Radar Astronomy Department of RRE, but was redundant by 1975. Well before this time Manchester University, with Professor Sir Bernard Lovell in charge of its Radio Astronomy Department, had become well-established as the national centre for radio astronomy research. As Dr Lovell, he had known Defford intimately from participation in many hours of flight trials during his wartime service at TRE. The disused telescopes passed into the control of the University who had plans for a national network of radio telescopes. Over the years, the rail tracks have been removed and one of the telescopes has been dismantled, but the remaining dish remains linked into the MERLIN network of seven radio telescopes. The Malvern establishment's presence on the airfield returned when RRE (which became RSRE in 1976) established a satellite communication centre located within a compound sited on one of the runways. Between 1990 and 2001, like the other MoD research establishments, RSRE had gradually been reduced in size and function, to become when privatised in 2001, a component of QinetiQ plc. QinetiQ withdrew from 'satcoms' activity in 2004, and the compound was taken over by West Mercia Constabulary, in whose control it remains. Most of the remainder of the old airfield, including those parts formerly in Croome Park and on Defford Common, is now in private ownership and not generally open to access.

Members of the RAF Defford Reunion Association, who gather each September, include a dwindling band of those who served and worked at Defford and Malvern, together with family and friends. In recent years, their annual meeting has been held in Croome Court itself. The RAF Defford Memorial on Defford village green was dedicated in 2002 and unveiled by Sir Bernard Lovell, wartime leader of the H_2S radar team at TRE Malvern. The Defford Airfield Heritage Group (DAHG) seeks to record and preserve the history of Defford airfield and radar research, recognised by and working closely with the National Trust. The RAF Defford Reunion Association merged in 2011 with DAHG. For further information on the activities of DAHG, which include on-going research into Boeing 247-D DZ203, see the Group's website – http://deffordairfieldheritagegroup.wordpress.com

Abbreviations

A&AEE	Aeroplane and Armament Experimental Establishment
ABLTAP	Automatic Blind Landing Technical Advisory Panel
ADEE	Air Defence Experimental Establishment
AI	Airborne Interception or Air Intercept
AID	Aeronautical Inspection Directorate
AIR	Aircraft Inspection Report (US)
AIS	Airborne Interception radar, S-band wavelength
AIX	Airborne Interception radar, X-band wavelength
AMAE	Air Member Aeronautical Engineering (Canada)
AMRE	Air Ministry Research Establishment
AMS	Air Member for Supply (Canada)
AMT	Air Member for Training (Canada)
AOC	Air Officer Commanding
AOS	Air Observer School (Canada)
APU	Auxiliary Power Unit
ARL	Aircraft Radar Laboratory at Wright Field (US)
ASE	Admiralty Signals Establishment
ASV	Air to Surface Vessel (radar)
ASVX	Air to Surface Vessel radar, X-band wavelength
ATC	Approved Type Certificate (US)
ATP	Air Technical Publications Board
AVM	Air Vice-Marshal
BA	Beam (or Blind) Approach (radar system)
BABS	Beam (or Blind) Approach Beacon System
BLEU	Blind Landing Experimental Unit
BAC	British Air Commission
BALPA	British Air Line Pilots' Association
BAT	Boeing Air Transport
BBC	British Broadcasting Corporation
BBRL	British Branch of the Radiation Laboratory
BCATP	British Commonwealth Air Training Plan
BEA	British European Airways
BOAC	British Overseas Airways Corporation
BPC	British Purchasing Commission
BSAA	British South American Airways

CAA	Civil Aeronautics Authority from 1938, Civil Aeronautics Administration from 1940 (US)
CAS	Chief of the Air Staff
CinC	Commander in Chief
CO	Commanding Officer
CRT	Cathode Ray Tube
DAHG	Defford Airfield Heritage Group
DCD	Directorate of Communications Development (of MAP)
DLH	Deutsches Lufthansa
DTD	Directorate of Technical Development (MAP)
FAA	Federal Aviation Administration (US)
FIU	Fighter Interception Unit
FRS	Fellow of the Royal Society
GAPAN	Guild of Air Pilots and Air Navigators
GCA	Ground Controlled Approach
GEC	General Electric Company (UK)
GL	Gun Laying (radar)
HMS	His Majesty's Ship (Royal Navy)
HWE	Home War Establishment (Canada)
IFF	Identification Friend from Foe
ILS	Instrument Landing System
LAC	Libraries and Archives Canada
MAP	Ministry of Aircraft Production
MIT	Massachusetts Institute of Technology
MoD	Ministry of Defence
MPRD	Metal Produce Recovery Depot
MU	Maintenance Unit (RAF)
NACA	National Advisory Committee on Aeronautics (US)
NAT	National Air Transport
NDRC	National Defence Research Council (US)
NRC	National Research Council (Canada)
OC	Officer Commanding
OIR	Operation Inspection Report (US)
ORB	Operations Record Book
OTU	Operational Training Unit
PAT	Pacific Air Transport
PCA	Pennsylvania-Central Airlines

PICAO	Provisional International Civil Aviation Organisation
RADORA	Radar Orbit and Approach
RAE	Royal Aircraft Establishment
RAF	Royal Air Force
RCAF	Royal Canadian Air Force
RNAS	Royal Naval Air Station
RRE	Radar Research Establishment (to 1957); Royal Radar Establishment, 1957 to 1976
RSRE	Royal Signals and Radar Establishment
SBA	Standard Beam (or Blind) Approach
SCR	Signal Corps Radio (US)
SDF	Special Duty Flight
TBO	Time Between Overhaul
TDE	Test and Development Establishment (Canada)
TDF	Test and Development Flight (Canada)
TFU	Telecommunications Flying Unit
TNA	The National Archives, Kew, England.
TRE	Telecommunications Research Establishment
UAL	United Air Lines
VHF	Very High Frequency (radio waves)
WAAF	Women's Auxiliary Air Force
WRNS	Women's Royal Naval Service

Index

Adams, Lt S, RN, 109
Aircraft
    Airspeed Envoy, 99, 109, 115
    Airspeed Oxford, 124, 126, 128, 141
    Armstrong Whitworth Whitley, 101
    Avro Anson, 24, 26, 51, 63, 67, 99, 108, 113
    Avro Lancaster, 126, 128, 150, 178
    Avro Tudor, 152
    Avro York, 51, 52
    BAC Trident, 158
    Blackburn Shark, 84
    Boeing B-17 Fortress, 125, 156, 184
    Boeing C-73, 130
    Boulton Paul Defiant, 84
    Bristol Beaufighter, 26, 88, 89
    Bristol Blenheim, 26, 74, 75, 79, 96
    Cessna T-50 Crane, 51, 72
    Consolidated B-24 Liberator, 125, 128, 136, 163
    De Havilland Queen Bee, 92
    Douglas A-26A, 69
    Douglas B-18, 21, 57, 59, 64, 68, 69, 70
    Douglas C-54, 124
    Douglas DC-1, 40
    Fairchild 91, 40, 41
    Fairchild Bolingbroke, 70, 86
    Fairey Barracuda, 96, 97, 104, 106, 118, 119, 195
    Fairey Battle, 26, 92
    Fairey Firefly, 96, 97, 118
    Fairey Fulmar, 97, 104, 110
    Grumman F6F Hellcat, 118
    Handley Page Halifax, 14, 114, 117
    Handley Page Harrow, 26, 27
    Handley Page Hermes, 152
    Handley Page Heyford, 23, 24
    Hawker Hurricane, 122
    Lockheed 10 Electra, 40, 41, 99
    Lockheed Hudson, 15, 106, 116
    Miles Messenger, 179
    North American Harvard, 131, 133, 156, 193
    Northrop Delta, 40
    Northrop P-61 Black Widow, 69
    Percival Vega Gull, 121
    Short S.30, 56
    Short Stirling, 126
    Sikorsky Hoverfly, 181
    Supermarine Spitfire, 122

    Supermarine Walrus, 14, 98
    Vickers Armstrong Warwick, 117
    Vickers Viking, 152
    Vultee V1A, 40, 41
    Westland Wallace, 23
Airfields
    Abingdon, 98
    Ballyherbert, 98
    Ballykelly, 98
    Boscombe Down, 78, 79, 89, 98, 109
    Boston Municipal Airport, 21, 22, 59, 64, 66, 67, 70, 71, 72, 86, 87, 187
    Bovingdon, 128, 130, 163
    Cambridge, 55, 93
    Carew Cheriton, 92
    Cheddington, 130
    Chivenor, 114
    Christchurch, 17, 26, 27, 72, 77, 78, 79, 80, 81, 82, 83, 84, 86, 87, 88, 89, 92, 161, 192
    Defford, 4, 9, 10, 16, 17, 19, 22, 27, 83, 89, 96, 97, 98, 99, 102, 104, 106, 108, 109, 110, 111, 112, 113, 114, 116, 117, 121, 122, 124, 125, 126, 128, 129, 130, 131, 132, 134, 135, 136, 139, 140, 141, 142, 148, 153, 155, 156, 158, 160, 161, 162, 163, 165, 168, 170, 171, 172, 173, 174, 176, 177, 178, 179, 180, 181, 182, 183, 184, 185, 187, 188, 190, 193, 195, 196, 198, 200
    Farnborough, 11, 78, 79, 126, 154, 165, 173, 176, 177, 178, 179, 180
    Ford, 77, 83, 85, 88, 172
    Halton, 130
    Harrowbeer, 98
    Heston, 130
    Hurn, 17, 26, 88, 89, 92, 93, 97, 98, 161
    Langford Lodge, 128
    Little Staughton, 179
    Macrihanish, 112
    Malton, Canada, 59, 60
    Manorbier, 92
    Montford Bridge, 183, 184, 185, 195
    Prestwick, 128, 171
    Rockcliffe, Canada, 60, 62, 64, 66, 67, 187
    Sleap, 11, 183, 184, 185, 195
    Speke, 72, 75, 78, 79, 130
    St Angelo, 98
    St Athan, 26

St Eval, 126
Stormy Down, 92
Tempsford, 117
Ternhill, 133
Trenton, Canada, 53, 60, 187
Valley, 99, 102, 110
Annis, Sqn Ldr, 160
Arnott, E W, 160
Ashfield, Flt Lt Glyn 'Jumbo', 83, 84
Atkinson, J R (Jimmy), 10, 97, 104, 107, 113
Babb, Charles H, 51, 52, 187
Baker, Fred - Boeing Service Engineer, 165, 166, 169, 170
Banner, Mr J, 110, 113
Barber, Fg Off Leonard C, 136, 139, 140, 141, 144, 146, 148, 153, 155, 158, 163, 171
Batt, Dr Reg, 10, 19, 80, 97, 104, 168, 207
Bawdsey Manor, 11, 21, 24, 26, 27
Bennett, AVM D 'Pathfinder', 148, 162
Berry, Peter, 10, 180, 181, 184
Birchall, M, 174
Blind Landing Experimental Unit (BLEU), 11, 173, 178, 179, 180
Boot, Howard, 21
Bottomley, Air Marshal Sir Norman, 170
Brady, Frank B, 9, 123, 124, 125, 128, 163
Briggs, Sqn Ldr F E R, 71, 72
British Commonwealth Air Training Plan (BCATP), 51, 59
Brown, Fg Off Frank, 93, 99, 100
Bruneval, 27
Canada Aviation and Space Museum, 196
Cheyenne, Wyoming, UAL Maintenance Base, 45, 47, 48, 49, 50, 52, 63, 64, 190
Christian, Flt Sgt, 93
Churchill, Winston S., 19, 55, 94
Clarke, Fg Off, 145, 155
Cobham, Sir Alan, 165
Cockcroft, Professor Sir John, 56, 82
Connor, Lt, USAAF, 125, 126, 128, 130, 163
Corson, Dr Dale, 71, 72, 75, 83, 86
Cox, Flt Sgt C W H, 27
Croome Park and Croome Court, 4, 10, 27, 104, 196, 198
Cunliffe-Owen Aircraft, 184
Cuse, Robert, 40, 41
Darwin, Dr, 85
Dee, Dr Philip, 82, 86, 102
Directorate of Communications Development (DCD), 132, 174, 176
Directorate of Technical Development (DTD), 174, 176

Dolbear, Flt Sgt, 138, 139, 140, 153, 154, 155
Doran, Lt USAAF, 104
Dowding, Air Chief Marshal Sir Hugh, 23, 24, 69, 70
Downing, Dr A.E., 86, 89
DuBridge, Lee, 56
Duckworth, John, 168
Elliot, Air Cdre, 83
Ellis, Flt Lt, 160, 161, 171
Evans, Air Chief Marshal Sir Donald Randell, 83, 88, 172
Ferrier, Gp Capt, 57
Fighter Interception Unit (FIU), 77, 83, 84, 85, 86, 88, 172
Fisher, Douglas, 10, 25, 80, 85, 99, 100, 101, 102, 106, 112, 114, 115
Fowler, Professor Ralph H, 55, 57, 60, 66
Frost, Major J.D., 27
Gallup, WRNS, 111
Gardner, Dr G, 154, 155, 178
Gilliard, Sqn Ldr, 113
Grenfell, Cdr, 113
Griffiths, Gp Capt Frank, 5, 10, 14, 16, 19, 78, 79, 82, 83, 88, 92, 93, 98, 99, 102, 108, 109, 111, 112, 117, 121, 122, 123, 124, 126, 128, 130, 133, 136, 138, 139, 140, 141, 142, 144, 145, 148, 153, 154, 155, 158, 160, 161, 162, 163, 173, 175, 178, 179, 181, 188, 189, 207
Hanbury Brown, Dr Robert, 109
Heath, J T (Jack), 24, 26, 57, 71, 72, 75, 79, 80, 81, 82, 83, 178
Henderson, John T, 55, 56, 82, 87
Hilbre Island, 99, 102
Hill, Professor Archibald Vivian, 55, 56
Hiscocks, R D, 63, 71
Hiscox, Sqn Ldr, 83
Hollowell, Flt Lt Kenneth, 10, 153, 155, 160, 161
Horner, Wg Cdr, 99
Inland Air Lines, 47, 52, 63
King, Gp Capt, 113, 115, 116
Knowles, Flt Lt Eric, 10, 160, 170, 171, 178
Lothian, Lord, 19
Lovell, Sir Bernard, 107, 198
Macguire, Sqn Ldr, 79
Mackenzie, C J, 56, 57, 66
Manion, Vern - Boeing photographer, 165, 166, 169, 170, 182, 189
Mar Cantabrico, Spanish ship, 41, 43
Massachusetts Institute of Technology (MIT), 21, 56, 69, 80, 86, 95

Mathias, Bill, 184
McDonald, Gp Capt John A, 5, 10, 14, 116, 121, 122, 126, 128, 131, 133, 135, 139, 140, 142, 144, 145, 146, 148, 150, 152, 153, 158, 160, 161, 165, 168, 171, 172, 178, 179, 180, 190
McNaughton, Gen A G L, 56
Milward, Lt Cdr A E, RNVR, later Sir Anthony Milward, 110, 162
Ministry of Aircraft Production (MAP), 88, 115, 131, 132, 133, 140, 141, 163, 173, 174, 183, 185
Monro, W L Jnr, 43, 45
Moore, LAC, 145
Moseley, Lt Col Francis L, 123, 124, 125, 126, 128, 129, 130, 131, 132, 135, 136, 142, 144, 146, 154, 158, 163
Mountford, Flt Lt R.H., 110
Mussell, L E, 97, 100, 101, 104
National Air and Space Museum of the Smithsonian Institution, 196
National Air Transport (NAT), 29, 33, 195
National Defence Research Council (NDRC), 21, 55, 56, 62, 71
National Research Council, Canada (NRC), 21, 55, 56, 60, 62, 66, 71, 85, 86, 87
National Trust, 10, 196, 198
Nestos, SS - Greek steamer, 102
Oliphant, Sir Mark, 112
Orford Ness, 23, 207
Palmer, W O, 145
Pearson, Wg Cdr, 83
Pennsylvania Airlines, 34, 37, 38, 49
Pennsylvania Central Airlines (PCA), 38, 39, 41, 43, 45, 49, 129, 195, 196
Perring, W G A, 173, 174
Pippet, Sqn Ldr, 93
Priest, D H, 27
Pringle, J.W.S., 86
Proctor, Sqn Ldr, 140
Radiation Laboratory, 21, 56, 69, 70, 80, 95
Randall, John, 21
Ratcliffe, J.A., 86
Reid, Wilfred T, 63, 66
Rennie, C A, 114
Renwick, Sir Robert, 162, 174
Ritson, F J U, 150
Rogers, Flt Lt, 133, 140, 145
Roosevelt, Franklin D., 19, 41, 55

Routledge, Plt Off, 99, 100
Royal Aircraft Establishment (RAE), 78, 126, 154, 173, 174, 175, 176, 177, 178, 179
Saltburn, HMS, 111
Schnorkel, breathing tube for U-boats, 118
Science Museum, Wroughton, 11, 195, 196
Skinner, Dr H.W.B., 86, 96, 97, 112
Slocombe, Flt Lt, 93
Southwell, J M, 160, 161
Specials Duties Flight (SDF), 26, 77, 78, 82
Stalker, George, 182, 183, 187, 190
Stauffacher, Capt., USAAF, 125, 128
Stedman, AVM, 66
Stewart, Flt Lt J. (Tom), 114, 126, 133, 141, 144, 148, 153, 160, 161
Swinton, Viscount, Secretary of State for Air, 158, 160
Taylor, Dr D, 9, 86
Telecommunications Flying Unit (TFU), 17, 19, 26, 27, 28, 72, 77, 80, 81, 88, 89, 92, 93, 96, 97, 98, 99, 101, 104, 110, 113, 116, 122, 132, 134, 142, 161, 165, 171, 173, 176, 180, 187, 188, 196
Telecommunications Research Establishment (TRE), 17, 19, 26, 27, 74, 75, 79, 80, 82, 83, 86, 92, 93, 95, 96, 97, 98, 101, 104, 107, 109, 110, 111, 112, 114, 115, 129, 131, 132, 140, 141, 150, 158, 168, 173, 174, 175, 176, 177, 179, 196
The Museum of Flight, 9, 196
Thelwell, J C, 160
Thompson, AVM Ronald Bain, 108, 109
Tizard, Sir Henry, 19, 21, 23, 24, 55, 56, 73, 80, 82, 83, 87, 94, 112
United Air Lines (UAL), 29, 33, 34, 35, 37, 38, 39, 41, 43, 45, 47, 130, 189, 192, 195, 196
Usher, Lt USAAC, 98
Vimalert, 40, 41
Warren, Dr John, 97
Watson-Watt, Sir Robert, 23, 158
Webb, Flt Lt W E P, 160
Wilkins, Arnold, 23, 24
Wirdnam, Fg Off Geoffrey, 110, 111
Worth Matravers, 17, 26, 74, 75, 86, 97
Wright Field, 128, 131, 132
Wyoming Air Service, 45, 47

References and Endnotes

[1] Reg Batt, *The Radar Army*, Robert Hale Ltd, London, 1991.

[2] Frank Griffiths, *Angel Visits – from Biplane to Jet*, Thomas Harmsworth Publishing, London, 1986.

[3] The Airspeed factory in the background of the photos of DZ203 was their 'Shadow' factory, the original main Airspeed factory being at Portsmouth Airport. The Christchurch one was a mail-order warehouse on the edge of Christchurch airfield requisitioned for Airspeed's use at the start of the war (Phil Butler).

[4] E.G. Bowen, *Radar Days*, Adam Hilger, 1987.

[5] The word 'radar' was coined by the US Navy to denote 'radio detection and ranging' and adopted by the British in 1943 (reference *'Transmission Lines'*, the Newsletter of the Defence Electronics History Society , Sept. 2011), but for convenience has been used from the outset in this book.

[6] Paddy Hazell, *The Hidden History of Orford Ness,* the History Press with the National Trust, Stroud 2010.

[7] W.H. Sleigh, *Aircraft for Airborne Radar Development*, RSRE, Malvern, 1986.

[8] F. Robert van der Linden, *The Boeing 247 – The First Modern Airliner*, University of Washington Press, Seattle and London, 1991.

[9] Henry H. Holden, *The Boeing 247 – The First Modern Commercial Airplane*, TAB Books, Blue Ridge Summit, PA, 1991.

[10] Of the two 247s for DLH, one entered service as D-AGAR, but was damaged beyond repair in May 1935 in a ground accident. The other, used for experimental work, crashed in August 1937.

[11] Peter M. Bowers, *Boeing Aircraft since 1916*, Putnam, 2nd edition 1989.

[12] Anon, 'Boeing 247', *Wingspan* No. 29, December 1985.

[13] A plaque which was attached to the rear cabin bulkhead of the aircraft while at TFU at RAF Defford around 1945, said *'Constructed Seattle USA 27th July 1933'* which may have been the date of the first flight, but if it was, the evidence for this date, which was more than ten years before the plaque was prepared, is not known.

[14] FAA File on NC13344, Maintenance Records, FAA Aircraft Registry, Oklahoma City, OK73125.

[15] Robert van der Linden, in a personal communication points out that the pilots were required to carry firearms to protect the mail.

[16] Jesus M.ª Salas Larrazabal, *Revista de Aeronautica*, No. 450, Vol. 38, May 1978, Madrid, pp. 389-394.

[17] Gerald Howson, *Aircraft of the Spanish Civil War*, Putnam, 1990.

[18] Anon, 'Those Versatile Vultees', *Air Enthusiast*, Vol. 3, No. 1, July 1972.

[19] Charles W. Cain, letter to the editor, *Air Pictorial*, Vol. 22, p.30, January 1960.

[20] Gerald Howson, *Aircraft of the Spanish Civil War*, Putnam, 1990.

[21] Gerald Howson, *Aircraft of the Spanish Civil War*, Putnam, 1990.

[22] F. Robert van der Linden, *The Boeing 247 – The First Modern Airliner*, University of Washington Press, Seattle and London, 1991.

[23] Department of National Defence, Canada: Minutes of the Supervisory Board, BCATP.

[24] File entitled 'Charles A Babb - Miscellaneous Aircraft Listings', in Record Group (RG) 28 series A, Volume 351, File 4-2-139, Libraries and Archives Canada (LAC)

[25] Phil Butler, personal communication.

[26] John Ellis, 'Civilian Aircraft in the RCAF', *Canadian Aviation Historical Society Journal*, Winter 1964.

[27] RCAF Aircraft Record Card, Canada Aviation & Space Museum.

[28] Mel Thistle (ed.), *The Mackenzie-McNaughton Wartime Letters*, University of Toronto Press, 1975.

[29] 'British Technical Mission', RG77 Acc 1988-89/045 Box 20 File 3-25-5-51, Libraries & Archives Canada (LAC).

[30] 'Co-operation with Microwave Research Laboratory, MIT', RG77 Acc 1985-86/178 Box 1 File 3-25-4-31, LAC.

[31] 'Researches – Committee on Experimental Flying', RG77 Acc 1988-89/046 Box 16 File 4-F5-9, LAC.

[32] 'Boeing 247-D – Generally', RG24 Vol. 5, 137 File 1021-9-122, LAC.

[33] E.G. Bowen, *Radar Days*, Adam Hilger, 1987.

[34] A brief history of the Test Flight at RCAF Station Rockcliffe, Ontario, its relationship with NRC, and subsequent name changes to the Test & Development Flight (1938), renamed Test & Development Establishment in December 1940, is summarised by John Bradley in *Aeromilitaria*, Vol 37, Issue 148, Winter Issue, December 2011, p.167.

[35] Terry Judge, personal communication.

[36] The author is indebted to Ron Henry for this explanation of radar technology in these two paragraphs and elsewhere; also reference was made to Ian White, *The History of Air Intercept (AI) Radar and the British Night-Fighter 1935-1959*, Pen & Sword, Barnsley, 2007, and J .G. Crowther, R. Whiddington, *Science at War*, HMSO, London, 1947.

[37] John Hamilton Parkin Papers, Department of Mechanical Engineering Progress Reports, National Research Council Archives.

[38] 'Research – Subcommittee on Moulded Wood', RG77, File 4-M5-9, LAC.

[39] Bruce G Heebink, *Fluid Pressure Moulding of Plywood*, US Dept. of Agriculture Forestry Service, University of Wisconsin, 1953.

[40] Henry Guelac, *Radar in World War II*, American Institute of Physics, 1987.

[41] Peter Gailson, *'Image and Logic - Laboratory War: Radar Philosophy and the Los Alamos Man'*, University of Chicago Press, 1997, p.248.

[42] 'Boeing Nose', RG77 Acc 1988-89/046 Box 34 File 4-M5-15, LAC.

[43] Arnold Hague, *The Allied Convoy System 1939-1945*, Vanwell Publications, 2000.

[44] Test & Development Establishment Diary, Microfilm C12217, LAC.

[45] E.G. Bowen, *Radar Days*, Adam Hilger, 1987.

[46] Ian White, *The History of Air Intercept (AI) Radar and the British Night-Fighter 1935-1959*, Pen & Sword, Barnsley, 2007.

[47] *Signals*, Vol. 5, Fighter Control and Interception, in 'The Second World War 1939-1945, Royal Air Force', Air Ministry (AHB), 1952.

[48] The organisation that re-assembled the Boeing was the 'Lockheed Aircraft Corporation's British Reassembly Division', which had been set up to re-assemble Hudson aircraft shipped from the USA but by the Summer of 1940 had received British contracts to assemble and do other preparation and modification work on many other American aircraft types (Phil Butler).

[49] Robert Buderi, *The Invention that Changed the World*, Simon & Schuster, 1996.

[50] The aircraft in which Griffiths is seated, is probably AE468, an ex-Belgian contract DB-7, converted to a Havoc I for the RAF, and fitted with AI radar. Griffiths flew AE468 on several occasions on AI trials between March and May 1941.

[51] Reg Batt, *The Radar Army*, Robert Hale Ltd, London, 1991.

[52] E.G. Bowen, letter from c/o CTE's Office, Ministry of Aircraft Production, to Dr. Darwin at NRC, dated 1st September 1941.

[53] F J Heath, letter to J T Henderson, RG77 Acc 85-86 Box 1 File 3-25-41, LAC.

[54] Peter W Moss, letter to *Air Pictorial*, Vol. 24, No. 10, October 1962, p.331.

[55] ORB of FIU Ford, AIR 29/27, The National Archive (TNA).

[56] FIU Report No. 85, 'American Ten Centimetre A.I. Equipment', 21st August 1941, in AIR 29/27, TNA.

[57] *Signals*, Vol. 5, Fighter Control and Interception, in 'The Second World War 1939-1945, Royal Air Force', Air Ministry (AHB), 1952, p.151.

[58] British Technical Mission, August 1940, RG77 Acc 88-89/045 Box 20 File 3-25-1-51, LAC.

[59] AI Technical Development, RG24 Vol. 5280 File S-34-2-15, LAC.

[60] H L Schultz, letter to J T Henderson dated 29th May 1941, RG77 Acc 85-86/178, Box 20 File 3-25-1-51, LAC.

[61] Sqn Ldr F E R Briggs, Report on Plastic Nose of Boeing 7655, RG77 Acc 88-89/046 Box 34 File 4-M5-15, LAC.

[62] R D Hiscox, report dated 19th June 1941, Inspection of Boeing Nose No. 1 at Boston on 13 June 1941, RG77 Acc 88-89/046 Box 34 File 4-M5-15, LAC.

[63] Mechanical Engineering Director's Reports, RG77 Acc 85-86/237, LAC.

[64] Ian White, *The History of Air Intercept (AI) Radar and the British Night Fighter 1935-1959*, Pen & Sword, Barnsley, 2007.

[65] ORB of FIU Ford, AIR 29/27, TNA.

[66] Norman Parker, letter to Neville Cullingford of the Royal Observer Corps Museum, 27th May 2010.

[67] Neville Cullingford of the Royal Observer Corps Museum, letter to the author 7th June 2010.

[68] Summary of aircraft allocation at TFU, 27th December 1941, AVIA 7/1603, TNA.

[69] TFU Report No. 73, period 16.2 to 15.3.1942, AVIA 7/1597, TNA.

[70] Aircraft Installation Conference, TRE Defford: Progress reports, 1940-43, AVIA 7/1047, TNA.

[71] David Zimmerman, *Top Secret Exchange – The Tizard Mission and the Scientific War*, McGill-Queen's University Press, Montreal & Kingston, Buffalo, 1996.

[72] J P Baxter, *Scientists Against Time*, Little Brown, Boston, 1946.

[73] 3 cm AI-ASV system for Firefly aircraft, 2nd February 1942, AVIA 26/5, TNA.

[74] Report TRE4/9/23, work in progress including Item 11. Basic Centimetre Work, Experimental 3 cm installation in Boeing aircraft, 5th May 1942, AVIA 7/1597, TNA.

[75] Ian White, *The History of Air Intercept (AI) Radar and the British Night Fighter 1935-1959*, Pen & Sword, Barnsley, 2007.

[76] Telecommunications Flying Unit: monthly progress reports 1941-1943, AVIA 7/1603, TNA.

[77] This photo, showing the interior of the Boeing as it was in 1942, was taken in early June. Frank Brown was killed on 16th August 1942, along with two fellow pilots from TFU, brothers Fg Off George Sellick and Fg Off Eric Sellick DFC, when Anson DJ184 broke up in flight.

[78] This photograph comes from a set taken by the Photographic Section of TRE, marked 'Blind bombing test on shipwreck in mouth of River Dee' (1942), and almost certainly depicts the SS *Nestos*. Smoke bombs are being dropped, and their fall photographed from a circling Anson.

[79] The 'Top Secret' category, and the use of the "/G" symbol is explained in *Aeromilitaria*, Vol 37 Issue 148, December 2011, Air Britain, p.182, quoting an MAP document on the subject.

[80] Summary of Boeing Flight Reports for Period July 7th – October 14th 1942, Report No. 8/R159/LEM (marked T1347), AVIA 26/349, TNA.

[81] H.A. Taylor, *Fairey Aircraft since 1915*, Putnam 1974.

[82] David J. Smith, *Action Stations 7, Military airfields of Scotland, the North East and Northern Ireland*, Patrick Stephens Ltd, Yeovil, 2nd edition reprinted 1993.

[83] State of aircraft serviceability at TRE Defford 1942-1944, AVIA 7/2687, TNA.

[84] Sir Bernard Lovell, *Echoes of War: The Story of H₂S Radar*, Taylor and Francis, Abingdon, 1991.

[85] R. Hanbury Brown, *Boffin*, IOP Publishing, Bristol, 1991.

[86] El was an abbreviation for an elevation aerial. '4 El' would be an elevation aerial for AI Mk IV, which operated in the 1.5 metre waveband.

[87] 'TX' was an abbreviation for 'transmitter'.

[88] ORB of RAF Andreas, AIR 28/1, TNA.

[89] Frank Griffiths, *Angel Visits – from Biplane to Jet*, Thomas Harmsworth Publishing, 1986.

[90] ORB RAF Chivenor, AIR 28/153, TNA.

[91] Director's Chart , TRE Malvern, March 1942, from the web-site 'Purbeck Radar', purbeckradar.org.uk

[92] MAP Form 2101 'Airframes' for Boeing 247-D DZ203.

[93] TFU Monthly Progress Meetings, 1943-44, AVIA 7/1604, TNA.

[94] Frank Griffiths, *Winged Hours*, William Kimber, London, 1981.

[95] The NF Mark II version of the Firefly involved extension of the fuselage which posed severe centre of gravity (C of G) problems. Subsequently, the requirement for a night fighter version of the Firefly was met by a simpler modification of the Mark I, resulting in the Firefly NF I.

[96] ASV Mk XI was fitted to the Fairey Swordfish III, to provide a versatile anti-submarine aircraft capable of flying off small escort carriers.

[97] Emmanuel Gustin, *British ASV Radars – Fighting the U-boats.* (online) Available at: www.uboat.net/allies/technical/uk_radars.htm.

[98] Ron Henry, personal communication

[99] Alan Hodgkin, *Chance and Design: reminiscences of science in peace and war*, Cambridge University Press, Cambridge, 1992.

[100] Sir Bernard Lovell, *Echoes of War: The Story of H₂S Radar*, Taylor and Francis, Abingdon, 1991.

[101] Air Chief Marshal (later Marshal of the Royal Air Force) Sir John Slessor had a long and distinguished career in the RAF. He was AOC Coastal Command from 1943, and CinC RAF Mediterranean and Middle East in 1944. He became Air Member for Personnel in 1945, and in that capacity marked the retirement of John McDonald in 1946 with a personal letter of thanks, which commenced with the hand-written salutation 'Dear Mac'. Slessor was appointed Chief of the Air Staff in 1950, and retired in 1953.

[102] A F Green (personal papers), 'Correspondence with Sir Stafford Cripps re aircraft losses in early radar trials at Defford', Imperial War Museum archives. Sir Stafford Cripps, who as Minister for Aircraft Production, had ultimate responsibility for TRE, concluded that the accident rate in relation to hours flown was no higher than might be expected.

[103] Frank B Brady, presentation to the 48th Annual Meeting, ION, 1st July 1992, Washington, DC: 'Soxo Air Sig S7 – ILS, From Early Development to an Enduring World Standard'.

[104] TFU Reports 1942 – 1944, AVIA 7/1598.

[105] John A McDonald, letter to *Flight International*, April 3rd 1964, p.737.

[106] Roger Mola, *History of Aircraft Landing Aids*, 2003. [online] Available at: http://www.centennialofflight.gov/essay/Government_Role/landing_nav/POL 14.htm

[107] Allocation of aircraft for RDF tests and trials at Defford 1943-1944, AVIA 7/2700, TNA.

[108] James C Fahey, *US Army Aircraft 1908-1946*, Ships and Aircraft, Broadway, NY 1946.

[109] C E Eval, P Halpert, *Automatic Landing Project*, Sperry Gyroscope Company, Garden City, NY, May 22 1944, AVIA 7/2729, TNA.

[110] The document states 'RAF' not as might be expected 'USAAF' presumably because it would be the RAF which would carry out the installation, possibly at Defford.

[111] 'Telecommunications Unit, Christchurch and Defford, later RAF Station Defford, 1941 October – 1945 December', AVIA 29/1195, TNA.

[112] TFU Report No. 70, in 'Telecommunications Flying Unit: Reports 1944-1945', AVIA 7/1599, TNA.

[113] K A Wood, TRE Report T1740, dated 11th October 1944, AVIA 26/742.

[114] Norman Dolbear, quoted in *Herefordshire & Worcestershire Airfields in the Second World War*, Robin J. Brooks, Countryside Books, 2006, pp. 57-58.

[115] Norman Dolbear, letter to Graham Evans, 17th May 2001.

[116] John A McDonald, letter to *Flight International*, April 3 1964, p.737.

[117] Gp Capt J A McDonald, *Aircraft Automatic Landing*, The Air BP Book of Flight, ed. J W R Taylor, Stanley Paul, London, 1960, pp 88-93.

[118] TFU Report No. 74, in 'Telecommunications Flying Unit: Reports 1944-1945', AVIA 7/1599, TNA.

[119] British Patent Application 22916/45. 'Improvements in and relating to radio control systems for aircraft and other vehicles', Flying Officer Leonard Charles Barber of Air Ministry, Adastral House, Kingsway, London WC2, 5th September 1945

[120] Papers of Leonard Charles Barber, deposited at Royal Air Force Museum, Hendon, accession no. X005-4863.

[121] Technical Advisory Panel No. 3: notes on meetings on automatic blind landing 1944-1945, AVIA 7/2730.

[122] Director's Chart , TRE Malvern, March 1942, from the web-site 'Purbeck Radar', purbeckradar.org.uk. Dr. F J U Ritson joined AMRE at Dundee in November 1939, and in 1941 worked with Lovell on 'lock-follow' and AI at Worth Matravers.

[123] Group Captain J A McDonald, 'Air BP' No. 17, c.1960 (copy in RAF Museum, Hendon, in papers of Leonard Charles Barber, accession number X005-4863).

[124] TFU Report No. 74, in Telecommunications Flying Unit: Reports, 1945, AVIA 7/1600, TNA.

[125] *Boeing News*, February 1947.

[126] 'Technical Advisory Panel No. 3: notes on meetings on automatic blind landing 1944-1945', AVIA 7/2730, TNA.

[127] Gp Capt J A McDonald, 'Aircraft Automatic Landing', *The Air BP Book of Flight*, ed. J W R Taylor, Stanley Paul, London, 1960, pp 88-93.

[128] Booklet, *3rd CERCA Conference, Malvern 1945*, in Telecommunications Research Establishment: Reports and papers 1938-46, AVIA 46/46, TNA

[129] Frank Griffiths, in a letter to his son Lloyd Cromwell Griffiths, 6th January 1993.

[130] Bill Webb, correspondence with Defford Airfield Heritage Group, and Oral History team of the Friends of Croome Park.

[131] Sir Robert Renwick, pre-war chairman of the London Electricity Board, Controller of Communications at the Air Ministry and of Communications Equipment at the Ministry of Aircraft Production from 1942 to 1945, whose responsibilities included placing of contracts with the electronics industry. He played a key role in the successful wartime development of radar.

[132] PICAO became (and still exists as) ICAO, a United Nations agency that sets International standards for Air Navigation.

[133] E H Putley, *Science comes to Malvern: TRE – a story of radar 1942-1953*, Aspect Design, Malvern, 2009.

[134] *Demonstration of Radio Aids to Civil Aviation*, HMSO, London, 1946.

[135] 'Telecommunications Flying Unit, Defford, 1946 January – 1950 December', AIR 29/1971, TNA.

[136] Lucero was a generic code name for a combined homing, beam approach and IFF interrogator for use with H_2S, ASV and AI radars, with the display appearing on the CRT of the parent equipment. It effectively included, amongst other functions, the role of Rebecca for 'Radar BA' landing aids, and some

versions were switchable to two Eureka channels. Developed for 10 cm waveband radars, it evolved further to be compatible with 3 cm radar.

[137] Automatic Blind Landing 1943-1945, AVIA 13/1142, TNA.

[138] Tom W Prescott, Head of BLEU, 1977: *History of BLEU 1945-1957*. Unpublished document via Antony Whitehead.

[139] Telecommunications Flying Unit, Defford 1946 January – 1950 December, AIR 29/1971, TNA.

[140] Peter Berry, *Paraffin Pete*, unpublished document, forwarded to the author November 2008.

[141] Peter Berry, 'My Time at RAF Defford', *Airfield Review*, March 2011.

[142] James Lees-Milne, *Caves of Ice – Diaries 1946-1947*, Michael Bloch, 1983.

[143] George Stalker, personal communication to Dennis Williams, 1998; also in information supplied by George Stalker for use in a display at the Pershore Heritage Centre, 34 High Street, Pershore, Worcestershire.

[144] Bruce Quarrie, *Action Stations 10, Supplement and Index*, Patrick Stephens, Cambridge, 1987.

[145] ORB MU No.34, RAF Montford Bridge, near Shrewsbury, Salop, 1946 January – 1950 December, AIR 29/1495, TNA.

[146] Dennis M Powell, 'The Boeing 247', *Air Pictorial,* Vol. 24, No. 7, July 1962; H.A. Taylor, 'Boeing's Trend Setting 247', *Air Enthusiast* No. 9, 1979; Henry M. Holden, *The Boeing 247 – The First Modern Commercial Airplane*, TAB Books, Blue Ridge Summit, PA, 1991.

[147] Bruce Robertson and 'Chronicler', 'US Aircraft in British Services 1914-1955, Part Nine', *Air Pictorial*, Vol. 19, November 1957.

[148] Peter Berry, 'The Origins of Blind Landing', *Journal of the American Aviation Historical Society,* pp 286-294, Winter 1997.

[149] George Stalker, personal communication to Dennis Williams; the words '14,000 flying hours' written (evidently by George Stalker) on the back of a photograph of DZ203 taken at Defford in April 1946.

[150] Boeing Nose, RG77 Acc 1988-89/046 Box 34 File 4-M5-15, LAC.

[151] Bruce Robertson, *Aircraft Camouflage and Markings 1907-1954*, Harleyford, Hemel Hempstead, 1954, p.102.

[152] Neil A MacDougall, Letter to *Air Pictorial*, Vol. 24, p. 389, 1962.

[153] Victor D. Seely, *Boeing's Pacesetting 247*, AAHS Journal, Winter 1964.

[154] TFU Report No. 74, in 'Telecommunications Flying Unit: Reports 1944-1945', AVIA 7/1599, TNA.